PRIMARY

Problem-solving in mathematics

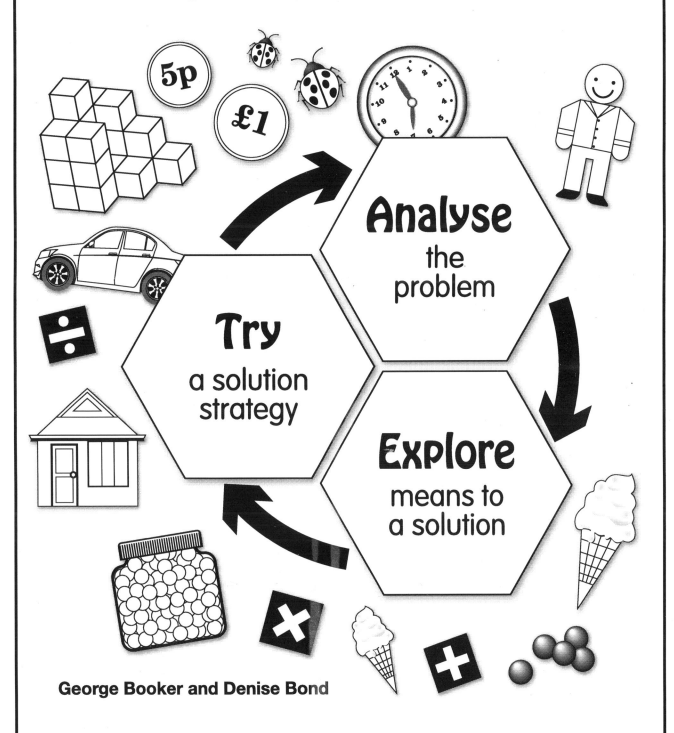

Analyse the problem

Explore means to a solution

Try a solution strategy

George Booker and Denise Bond

6032UK

Problem-solving in mathematics
(Book C)

Published by R.I.C. Publications® 2008

Republished under licence by Prim-Ed Publishing 2009

Copyright© George Booker and Denise Bond 2007

ISBN 978-1-84654-184-1

PR–6032

Titles available in this series:

Problem-solving in mathematics *(Book A)*
Problem-solving in mathematics *(Book B)*
Problem-solving in mathematics *(Book C)*
Problem-solving in mathematics *(Book D)*
Problem-solving in mathematics *(Book E)*
Problem-solving in mathematics *(Book F)*
Problem-solving in mathematics *(Book G)*

Internet websites

In some cases, websites or specific URLs may be recommended. While these are checked and rechecked at the time of publication, the publisher has no control over any subsequent changes which may be made to webpages. It is *strongly* recommended that the class teacher checks *all* URLs before allowing pupils to access them.

View all pages online

Books A–G of **Problem-solving in mathematics** have been developed to provide a rich resource for teachers of pupils from the early years to the end of primary school and into secondary school. The series of problems, discussions of ways to understand what is being asked and means of obtaining solutions have been built up to improve the problem-solving performance and persistence of all pupils. It is a fundamental belief of the authors that it is critical that pupils and teachers engage with a few complex problems over an extended period rather than spend a short time on many straightforward 'problems' or exercises. In particular, it is essential to allow pupils time to review and discuss what is required in the problem-solving process before moving to another and different problem. This book includes extensive ideas for extending problems and solution strategies to assist teachers in implementing this vital aspect of mathematics in their classrooms. Also, the problems have been constructed and selected over many years' experience with pupils at all levels of mathematical talent and persistence, as well as in discussions with teachers in classrooms and professional learning and university settings.

Problem-solving does not come easily to most people, so learners need many experiences engaging with problems if they are to develop this crucial ability. As they grapple with problem meaning and find solutions, pupils will learn a great deal about mathematics and mathematical reasoning—for instance, how to organise information to uncover meanings and allow connections among the various facets of a problem to become more apparent, leading to a focus on organising what needs to be done rather than simply looking to apply one or more strategies. In turn, this extended thinking will help pupils make informed choices about events that affect their lives and to interpret and respond to the decisions made by others at school, in everyday life and in further study.

Pupil and teacher pages

The pupil pages present problems chosen with a particular problem-solving focus and draw on a range of mathematical understandings and processes. For each set of related problems, teacher notes and discussion are provided, as well as indications of how particular problems can be examined and solved. Answers to the more straightforward problems and detailed solutions to the more complex problems ensure appropriate explanations and suggest ways in which problems can be extended. Related problems occur on one or more pages that extend the problem's ideas, the solution processes and pupils' understanding of the range of ways to come to terms with what the problems are asking.

At the top of each teacher page, a statement highlights the particular thinking that the problems will demand, together with an indication of the mathematics that might be needed and a list of materials that can be used in seeking a solution. A particular focus for the page or set of three pages of problems then expands on these aspects. Each book is organised so that when a problem requires complicated strategic thinking, two or three problems occur on one page (supported by a teacher page with detailed discussion) to encourage pupils to find a solution together with a range of means that can be followed. More often, problems are grouped as a series of three interrelated pages where the level of complexity gradually increases, while the associated teacher page examines one or two of the problems in depth and highlights how the other problems might be solved in a similar manner.

Each teacher page concludes with two further aspects critical to the successful teaching of problem-solving. A section on likely difficulties points to reasoning and content inadequacies that experience has shown may well impede pupils' success. In this way, teachers can be on the lookout for difficulties and be prepared to guide pupils past these potential pitfalls. The final section suggests extensions to the problems to enable teachers to provide several related experiences with problems of these kinds in order to build a rich array of experiences with particular solution methods; for example, the numbers, shapes or measurements in the original problems might change but leave the means to a solution essentially the same, or the context may change while the numbers, shapes or measurements remain the same. Then numbers, shapes or measurements *and* the context could be changed to see how the pupils handle situations that appear different but are essentially the same as those already met and solved.

Other suggestions ask pupils to make and pose their own problems, investigate and present background to the problems or topics to the class, or consider solutions at a more general level (possibly involving verbal descriptions and eventually pictorial or symbolic arguments). In this way, not only are pupils' ways of thinking extended but the problems written on one page are used to produce several more problems that utilise the same approach.

Mathematics and language

The difficulty of the mathematics gradually increases over the series, largely in line with what is taught at the various year levels, although problem-solving both challenges at the point of the mathematics that is being learned and provides insights and motivation for what might be learned next. For example, the computation required gradually builds from additive thinking, using addition and subtraction separately and together, to multiplicative thinking, where multiplication and division are connected conceptions. More complex interactions of these operations build up over the series as the operations are used to both come to terms with problems' meanings and to achieve solutions. Similarly, two-dimensional geometry is used at first but extended to more complex uses over the range of problems, then joined by interaction with three-dimensional ideas. Measurement, including chance and data, also extends over the series from length to perimeter, and from area to surface area and volume, drawing on the relationships among these concepts to organise solutions as well as give an understanding of the metric system. Time concepts range from interpreting timetables using 12-hour and 24-hour clocks, while investigations related to mass rely on both the concept itself and practical measurements.

The language in which the problems are expressed is relatively straightforward, although this too increases in complexity and length of expression across the books in terms of both the context in which the problems are set and the mathematical content that is required. It will always be a challenge for some pupils to 'unpack' the meaning from a worded problem, particularly as the problems' context, information and meanings expand. This ability is fundamental to the nature of mathematical problem-solving and needs to be built up with time and experiences rather than be diminished or left out of the problems' situations. One reason for the suggestion that pupils work in groups is to allow them to share and assist each other with the tasks of discerning meanings and ways to tackle the ideas in complex problems through discussion, rather than simply leaping into the first ideas that come to mind (leaving the full extent of the problem unrealised).

An approach to solving problems

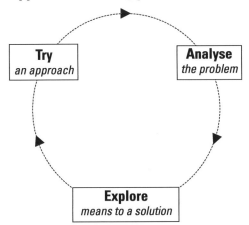

The careful, gradual development of an ability to analyse problems for meaning, organising information to make it meaningful and to make the connections among the problems more meaningful in order to suggest a way forward to a solution is fundamental to the approach taken with this series, from the first book to the last. At first, materials are used explicitly to aid these meanings and connections; however, in time they give way to diagrams, tables and symbols as understanding and experience of solving complex, engaging problems increases. As the problem forms expand, the range of methods to solve problems is carefully extended, not only to allow pupils to successfully solve the many types of problems, but also to give them a repertoire of solution processes that they can consider and draw on when new situations are encountered. In turn, this allows them to explore one or another of these approaches to see whether each might furnish a likely result. In this way, when they try a particular method to solve a new problem, experience and analysis of the particular situation assists them in developing a full solution.

Not only is this model for the problem-solving process helpful in solving problems, it also provides a basis for pupils to discuss their progress and solutions and determine whether or not they have fully answered a question. At the same time, it guides teachers' questions of pupils and provides a means of seeing underlying mathematical difficulties and ways in which problems can be adapted to suit particular needs and extensions. Above all, it provides a common framework for discussions between a teacher and group or whole class to focus on the problem-solving process rather than simply on the solution of particular problems. Indeed, as Alan Schoenfeld, in Steen L. (Ed) *Mathematics and democracy* (2001), states so well, in problem-solving:

getting the answer is only the beginning rather than the end ... an ability to communicate thinking is equally important.

We wish all teachers and pupils who use these books success in fostering engagement with problem-solving and building a greater capacity to come to terms with and solve mathematical problems at all levels.

George Booker and Denise Bond

CONTENTS

Foreword .... iii – v

Contents vi

Introduction .... vii – xix

Teacher notes 2

Larger shapes 3

Grid fun 1 4

Grid fun 2 5

Teacher notes 6

The big race 7

Teacher notes 8

What's my number? 9

Missing numbers 10

What's my age? 11

Teacher notes 12

At the beach 13

At the party 14

In the garden 15

Teacher notes 16

How many digits? 17

Teacher notes 18

Tangrams 1 19

Tangrams 2 20

Tangrams 3 21

Teacher notes 22

Magic squares 1 23

Magic squares 2 24

Magic circles 25

Teacher notes 26

Tuckshop 27

Teacher notes 28

Window panes 1 29

Drive time 30

Window panes 2 31

Teacher notes 32

Kangaroo mobs 33

Cooking time 34

Duck pond 35

Teacher notes 36

Bird trees 37

Teacher notes 38

Animal trails 39

Balance the books 40

Taking time 41

Teacher notes 42

Party food 43

How long? 44

At the shops 45

Teacher notes 46

Toothpicks 47

Building with cubes 48

Stacking cubes 49

Teacher notes 50

How many? 51

Solutions 52–55

Tangram resource page 56

10 mm x 10 mm grid resource page 57

15 mm x 15 mm grid resource page 58

Triangular grid resource page 59

Triangular isometric resource page 60

Square isometric resource page 61

4-digit number expander resource page (x 5) 62

Problem-solving and mathematical thinking

> *By learning problem-solving in mathematics, pupils should acquire ways of thinking, habits of persistence and curiosity, and confidence in unfamiliar situations that will serve them well outside the mathematics classroom. In everyday life and in the workplace, being a good problem solver can lead to great advantages.*
>
> **NCTM-Principles and standards for school mathematics (2000, p. 52)**

Problem-solving lies at the heart of mathematics. New mathematical concepts and processes have always grown out of problem situations and pupils' problem-solving capabilities develop from the very beginning of mathematics learning. A need to solve a problem can motivate pupils to acquire new ways of thinking as well as come to terms with concepts and processes that might not have been adequately learned when first introduced. Even those who can calculate efficiently and accurately are ill prepared for a world where new and adaptable ways of thinking are essential if they are unable to identify which information or processes are needed.

On the other hand, pupils who can analyse the meaning of problems, explore means to a solution and carry out a plan to solve mathematical problems have acquired deeper and more useful knowledge than simply being able to complete calculations, name shapes, use formulas to make measurements or determine measures of chance and data. It is critical that mathematics teaching focuses on enabling all pupils to become both able and willing to engage with and solve mathematical problems.

Well-chosen problems encourage deeper exploration of mathematical ideas, build persistence and highlight the need to understand thinking strategies, properties and relationships. They also reveal the central role of *sense making* in mathematical thinking—not only to evaluate the need for assessing the reasonableness of an answer or solution, but also the need to consider the interrelationships among the information provided with a problem situation. This may take the form of number sense, allowing numbers to be represented in various ways and operations to be interconnected; through spatial sense that allows the visualisation of a problem in both its parts and whole; to a sense of measurement across length, area, volume and chance and data.

Problem-solving

A problem is a task or situation for which there is no immediate or obvious solution, so that *problem-solving* refers to the processes used when engaging with this task. When problem-solving, pupils engage with situations for which a solution strategy is not immediately obvious, drawing on their understanding of concepts and processes they have already met, and will often develop new understandings and ways of thinking as they move towards a solution. It follows that a task that is a problem for one pupil may not be a problem for another and that a situation that is a problem at one level will only be an exercise or routine application of a known means to a solution at a later time.

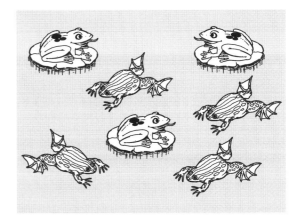

For a pupil aged 5-6 years, sorting out the information about being on the lily pad and being in the water may take some consideration and require counters to represent the numbers and find the answer. For children in the middle primary years, understanding of the addition concept and knowledge of the addition facts would lead them immediately to think about the sum of 3 and 4 and come up with the solution of 7 frogs.

As the world in which we live becomes ever more complex, the level of mathematical thinking and problem-solving needed in life and in the workplace has increased considerably. Those who understand and can use the mathematics they have learned will have opportunities opened to them that those who do not develop these ways of thinking will not. To enable pupils to thrive in this changing world, attitudes and ways of knowing that enable them to deal with new or unfamiliar tasks are now as essential as the procedures that have always been used to handle familiar operations readily and efficiently. Such an attitude needs to develop from the beginning of mathematics learning as pupils form beliefs about meaning, the notion of taking control over the activities they engage with and the results they obtain, and as they build an inclination to try different approaches. In other words, pupils need to see mathematics as a way of thinking rather than a means of providing answers to be judged right or wrong by a teacher, textbook or some other external authority. They must be led to focus on means of solving problems rather than on particular answers so that they understand the need to determine the meaning of a problem before beginning to work on a solution.

In a car race, Jordan started in fourth place. During the race, he was passed by six cars. How many cars does he need to pass to win the race?

In order to solve this problem, it is not enough to simply use the numbers that are given. Rather, an analysis of the race situation is needed first to see that when Jordan started, there were 3 cars ahead

of him. When another 6 cars passed him, there were now 9 ahead of him. If he is to win, he needs to pass all 9 cars. The 4 and 6 implied in the problem were not used at all! Rather, a diagram or the use of materials is needed first to interpret the situation and then see how a solution can be obtained.

However, many pupils feel inadequate when they encounter problem-solving questions. They seem to have no idea of how to go about finding a solution and are unable to draw on the competencies they have learned in number, space and measurement. Often these difficulties stem from underdeveloped concepts for the operations, spatial thinking and measurement processes. They may also involve an underdeveloped capacity to read problems for meaning and a tendency to be led astray by the wording or numbers in a problem situation. Their approach may then simply be to try a series of guesses or calculations rather than consider using a diagram or materials to come to terms with what the problem is asking and using a systematic approach to organise the information given and required in the task. It is this ability to analyse problems that is the key to problem-solving, enabling decisions to be made about which mathematical processes to use, which information is needed and which ways of proceeding are likely to lead to a solution.

Making sense in mathematics

Making sense of the mathematics being developed and used must be seen as the central concern of learning. This is important, not only in coming to terms with problems and means to solutions, but also in terms of bringing meaning, representations and relationships in mathematical ideas to the forefront of thinking about and dealing with mathematics. Making sensible interpretations of any results and determining which of several possibilities is more or equally likely is critical in problem-solving.

Number sense, which involves being able to work with numbers comfortably and competently, is important in many aspects of problem-solving, in making judgments, interpreting information and communicating ways of thinking. It is based on a full understanding of numeration concepts such as zero, place value and the renaming of numbers in equivalent forms, so that 207 can be seen as 20 tens and 7 ones as well as 2 hundreds and 7 ones (or that $\frac{5}{2}$, 2.5 and $2\frac{1}{2}$ are all names for the same fraction amount). Automatic, accurate access to basic facts also underpins number sense, not as an end in itself, but rather as a means of combining with numeration concepts to allow manageable mental strategies and fluent processes for larger numbers. Well-understood concepts for the operations are essential in allowing relationships within a problem to be revealed and taken into account when framing a solution.

> **Number sense requires:**
>
> - understanding relationships among numbers
> - appreciating the relative size of numbers
> - a capacity to calculate and estimate mentally
> - fluent processes for larger numbers and adaptive use of calculators
> - an inclination to use understanding and facility with numeration and computation in flexible ways.

The following problem highlights the importance of these understandings.

There were 317 people at the New Year's Eve party on 31 December. If each table could seat 5 couples, how many tables were needed?

Reading the problem carefully shows that each table seats five couples or 10 people. At first glance, this problem might be solved using division; however, this would result in a decimal fraction, which is not useful in dealing with people seated at tables:

$$10\overline{)317} \text{ is } 31.7$$

In contrast, a full understanding of numbers allows 317 to be renamed as 31 tens and 7 ones:

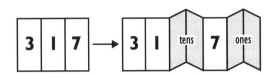

This provides for all the people at the party and analysis of the number 317 shows that there have to be at least 32 tables for everyone to have a seat and allow partygoers to move around and sit with others during the evening. Understanding how to *rename* a number has provided a direct solution without any need for computation. It highlights how coming to terms with a problem and integrating this with number sense provides a means of solving the problem more directly and allows an appreciation of what the solution might mean.

Spatial sense is equally important, as information is frequently presented in visual formats that need to be interpreted and processed, while the use of diagrams is often essential in developing conceptual understanding across all aspects of mathematics. Using diagrams, placing information in tables or depicting a systematic way of dealing with the various possibilities in a problem assist in visualising what is happening. It can be a very powerful tool in coming to terms with the information in a problem, and it provides insight into ways to proceed to a solution.

> **Spatial sense involves:**
>
> - a capacity to visualise shapes and their properties
> - determining relationships among shapes and their properties
> - linking two-dimensional and three-dimensional representations
> - presenting and interpreting information in tables and lists
> - an inclination to use diagrams and models to visualise problem situations and applications in flexible ways.

The following problem shows how these understandings can be used.

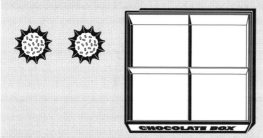

Cathy has 2 chocolates and 1 box. In how many different ways can she place the chocolates in the box?

Reading the problem carefully shows that only two spaces in the box can be used each time and that no use of the spaces can be duplicated. A systematic approach, placing one chocolate in a fixed position and varying the other spaces will provide a solution; however, care will be needed to see that the same placement has not already occurred:

There are six possible arrangements. The placement of objects on the diagram has provided a solution, highlighting how coming to terms with a problem and integrating this with spatial sense allows a systematic analysis of all the possibilities.

Similar thinking is used with arrangements of two-dimensional and three-dimensional shapes and in visualising how they can fit together or be taken apart.

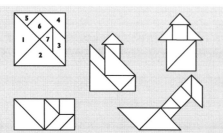

Which of these shapes can be made using all of the tangram pieces?

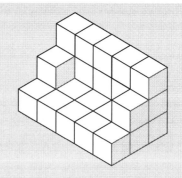

How many cubes are needed to make this shape?

Measurement sense is dependent on both number sense and spatial sense, since attributes that are one-, two- or three-dimensional are quantified to provide both exact and approximate measures and allow comparison. Many measurements use aspects of space (length, area, volume), while others use numbers on a scale (time, mass, temperature). Money can be viewed as a measure of value and uses numbers more directly, while practical activities such as map reading and determining angles require a sense of direction as well as gauging measurement. The coordination of the thinking for number and space, along with an understanding of how the metric system builds on place value, zero and renaming, is critical in both building measurement understanding and using it to come to terms with and solve many practical problems and applications.

Measurement sense includes:

- understanding how numeration and computation underpin measurement
- extending relationships from number understanding to the metric system
- appreciating the relative size of measurements
- a capacity to use calculators, mental or written processes for exact and approximate calculations
- an inclination to use understanding and facility with measurements in flexible ways.

The following problem shows how these understandings can be used.

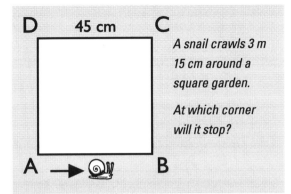

D   45 cm   C

A snail crawls 3 m 15 cm around a square garden.

At which corner will it stop?

A → 🐌   B

Carefully reading the problem shows that the snail will travel 45 cm as it moves along each side of the square. In order to come to terms with what is needed, 3 m 15 cm needs to be renamed as 315 cm. The distances the snail travels along each side can then be totalled until 315 cm is reached. It can also be inferred that it will travel along some sides more than once as the distance around the outside of the square is 180 cm. At this point, the snail will be back at A. Travelling a further 45 cm will take it to B, a distance of 225 cm. At C it will have travelled 270 cm and it will have travelled 315 cm (or 3 m 15 cm) when it reaches D for the second time.

By using an understanding of the problem situation, a diagram has been integrated with the knowledge of metres and centimetres and a capacity to calculate mentally using addition and multiplication to provide an appropriate solution. Both spatial sense and number sense have been used to understand the problem and suggest a means to a solution.

Data sense is an outgrowth of measurement sense and refers to an understanding of the way number sense, spatial sense and a sense of measurement work together to deal with situations where patterns need to be discerned among data or when likely outcomes need to be analysed. This can occur among frequencies in data or possibilities in chance.

Data sense involves:

- understanding how numeration and computation underpin the analysis of data
- appreciating the relative likelihood of outcomes
- a capacity to use calculators or mental and written processes for exact and approximate calculations
- presenting and interpreting data in tables and graphs
- an inclination to use understanding and facility with number combinations and arrangements in flexible ways.

The following problem shows how these understandings can be used.

You are allowed 3 scoops of ice-cream: 1 chocolate, 1 vanilla and 1 strawberry. How many different ways can the scoops be placed on a cone?

There are six possibilities for placing the scoops of ice-cream on a cone. Systematically treating the possible placements one at a time highlights how the use of a diagram can account for all possible arrangements.

This problem also shows how **patterning** is another aspect of sense-making in mathematics. Often a problem calls on discerning a pattern in the placement of materials, the numbers involved in the situation or the possible arrangements of data or outcomes to determine a likely solution. Being able to see patterns is also very helpful in getting an immediate solution or understanding whether or not a solution is complete. Allied to patterning are notions of symmetry, repetition and extending ideas to more general cases. All of these aspects of mathematical sense-making are critical to developing the thinking on which problem-solving depends, as well as solving problems per se.

As more experience in solving problems is gained, an ability to see patterns in what is occurring will also allow solutions to be obtained more directly and help in seeing the relationship between a new problem and one that has been solved previously. It is this ability to relate problem types, even when the context appears to be quite different, that often distinguishes a good problem solver from one who is more hesitant.

Building a problem-solving process

While the teaching of problem-solving has often centred on the use of particular strategies that could apply to various classes of problems, many pupils are unable to access and use these strategies to solve problems outside of the teaching situations in which they were introduced. Rather than acquire a process for solving problems, they may attempt to memorise a set of procedures and view mathematics as a set of learned rules where success follows the use of the right procedure to the numbers given in the problem. Any use of strategies may be based on familiarity, personal preference or recent exposure rather than through a consideration of the problem to be solved. A pupil may even feel it is sufficient to have only one strategy and that the strategy should work all of the time—and if it doesn't, then the problem can't be solved.

In contrast, observation of successful problem-solvers shows that their success depends more on an analysis of the problem itself—what is being asked, what information might be used, what answer might be likely and so on—so that a particular approach is used only after the intent of the problem is determined. Establishing the meaning of the problem before any plan is drawn up or work on a solution begins is critical. Pupils need to see that discussion about the problem's meaning, and the ways of obtaining a solution, must take precedence over a focus on the answer. Using collaborative groups when problem-solving, rather than tasks assigned individually, is an approach that helps to develop this disposition.

Looking at a problem and working through what is needed to solve it will shed light on the problem-solving process.

On Saturday, Peta went to the shopping centre to buy a new outfit to wear at her friend's birthday party. She spent half of her money on a dress and then one-third of what she had left on a pair of sandals. After her purchases, she had £60.00 left in her purse. How much money did she have to start with?

By reading the problem carefully, it can be determined that Peta had an original amount of money to spend. She spent some on a dress and some on shoes and then had £60.00 left. All of the information required to solve the problem is available and no further information is needed. The question at the end asks how much money did she start with, but really the problem is how much did she spend on the dress and then on the sandals.

The discussion of this problem has served to identify the key element within the problem-solving process; it is necessary to analyse the problem to unfold its meanings and discover what needs to be considered. What the problem is asking is rarely found in the question in the problem statement. Instead, it is necessary to look below the surface level of the problem and come to terms with the problem's structure. Reading the problem aloud, thinking of previous problems and other similar problems, selecting important information from the problem that may be useful, and discussion of the problem's meaning are all essential.

The next step is to explore possible ways to solve the problem. If the analysis stage has been completed, then ways in which the problem might be solved will emerge.

It is here that strategies, and how they might be useful to solving a problem, can arise. However, most problems can be solved in a variety of ways, using different approaches, and pupils need to be encouraged to select a method that makes sense and appears achievable.

Ways that may come to mind during the analysis include:

- *Materials* – Base 10 materials could be used to represent the money spent and to help the pupil work backwards through the problem from when Peta had £60.00 left.

- *Try and adjust* – Select an amount that Peta might have taken shopping, try it in the context of the question, examine the resulting amounts, and then adjust them, if necessary, until £60.00 is the result.

- *Backtrack using the numbers* – The sandals were one-third of what was left after the dress, so the £60.00 would be two-thirds of what was left. Together, these two amounts would match the cost of the dress.

- *Use a diagram* to represent the information in the problem.

- *Think of a similar problem* – For example, it is like the car race problem in that the relative portions (places) are known and the final result (money left, winning position) are given.

Now *one* of the possible means to a solution can be selected to try. Backtracking shows that £60 was two-thirds of what she had left, so the sandals (which are one-third of what she had left) must have cost £30. Together, these are half of what Peta took, which is also the cost of the dress. As the dress cost £90, Peta took £180 to spend.

Materials could also have been used with which to work backwards: 6 tens represent the £60 left, so the sandals would cost 3 tens and the dress 9 tens—she took 18 tens or £180 shopping.

Another way to solve the problem is with a diagram. If we use a rectangle to represent how much money Peta took with her, we can show by shading how much she spent on a dress and sandals:

Total amount available to spend:

She spent half of her money on a dress.

She then spent one-third of what she had left on sandals, which has minimised and simplified the calculations.

At this point she had £60 left, so the two unshaded parts must be worth £60 or £30 per part—which has again minimised and simplified the calculations.

| | £30 | £30 |

Each of the six equal parts represents £30, so Peta took £180 to spend.

Having tried an idea, an answer needs to be analysed in the light of the problem in case another solution is required. It is essential to compare an answer to the original analysis of the problem to determine whether the solution obtained is reasonable and answers the problem. It will also raise the question as to whether other answers exist and even whether there might be other solution strategies. In this way the process is cyclic and should the answer be unreasonable, then the process would need to begin again.

We believe that Peta took £180 to shop with. She spent half (or £90) on a dress, leaving £90. She spent one-third of the £90 on sandals (£30), leaving £60. Looking again at the problem, we see that this is correct and the diagram has provided a direct means to the solution that has minimised and simplified the calculations.

Thinking about the various ways this problem was solved highlights the key elements within the problem-solving process. When starting the process, it is necessary to *analyse* the problem to unfold its layers, discover its structure and understand what the problem is really asking. Next, all possible ways to solve the problem are *explored* before one, or a combination of ways, are selected to *try*. Finally, once something is tried, it is important to check the solution in relation to the problem to see if the solution is reasonable. This process highlights the cyclic nature of problem-solving and brings to the fore the importance of understanding the problem (and its structure) before proceeding. This process can be summarised as:

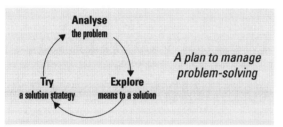

A plan to manage problem-solving

This model for problem-solving provides pupils with a means of talking about the steps they take whenever they have a problem to solve: Discussing how they initially analysed the problem, explored various ways that might provide a solution, and then tried one or more possible solution paths to obtain a solution—which they then analysed for completeness and sense-making—reinforces the very methods that will give them success on future problems. This process brings to the fore the importance of understanding the problem and its structure before proceeding.

Further, returning to an analysis of any answers and solution strategies highlights the importance of reflecting on what has been done. Taking time to reflect on any plans drawn up, processes followed and strategies used brings out the significance of coming to terms with the nature of the problem, as well as the value and applicability of particular approaches that might be used with other problems. Thinking of how a related problem was solved is often the key to

solving another problem at a later stage. It allows the thinking to be carried over to the new situation in a way that simply trying to think of the strategy used often fails to reveal. Analysing problems in this way also highlights that a problem is not solved until the answer obtained can be justified. Learning to reflect on the *whole* process leads to the development of a deeper understanding of problem-solving, and time must be allowed for reflection and discussion to fully build mathematical thinking.

Managing a problem-solving programme

Teaching problem-solving differs from many other aspects of mathematics in that collaborative work can be more productive than individual work. Pupils who may be tempted to quickly give up when working on their own can be encouraged to see ways of proceeding when discussing a problem in a group; therefore building greater confidence in their capacity to solve problems and learning the value of persisting with a problem in order to tease out what is required. What is discussed with their peers is more likely to be recalled when other problems are met, while the observations made in the group increase the range of approaches that a pupil can access. Thus, time has to be allowed for discussion and exploration rather than insisting that pupils spend 'time on task' as for routine activities.

Correct answers that fully solve a problem are always important, but developing a capacity to use an effective problem-solving process needs to be the highest priority. A pupil who has an answer should be encouraged to discuss his or her solution with others who believe they have a solution, rather than tell his or her answer to another pupil or simply move on to another problem. In particular, explaining to others why he or she believes an answer is reasonable, as well as why it provides a solution, gets other pupils to focus on the entire problem-solving process rather than just quickly getting an answer.

Expressing an answer in a sentence that relates to the question stated in the problem also encourages reflection on what was done and ensures that the focus is on solving the problem rather than providing an answer. These aspects of the teaching of problem-solving should then be taken further, as particular groups discuss their solutions with the whole class and all pupils are able to participate in the discussion of the problem. In this way, problem-solving as a way of thinking comes to the fore, rather than focusing on the answers as the main aim of their mathematical activities.

Questions must encourage pupils to explore possible means to a solution and try one or more of them, rather than point to a particular procedure. It can also help pupils to see how to progress in their thinking, rather than get into a loop where the same steps are repeated over and over. While having too many questions that focus on the way to a solution may end up removing the problem-solving aspect from the question, having too few may cause pupils to become frustrated with the task and think that it is beyond them. Pupils need to experience the challenge of problem-solving and gain pleasure from working through the process that leads to a full solution. Taking time to listen to pupils as they try out their ideas, without comment or without directing them to a particular strategy, is also important. Listening provides a sense of how pupils' problem-solving is developing, as assessing this aspect of mathematics can be difficult. After all, solving one problem will not necessarily lead to success on the next problem, nor will difficulty with a particular problem mean that the problems that follow will also be as challenging.

A teacher also may need to extend or adapt a given problem to ensure the problem-solving process is understood and can be used in other situations, instead of moving on to a different problem in another area of mathematics learning. This can help pupils to understand the significance of asking questions of a problem, as well as seeing how a way of thinking can be adapted to other related problems. Having pupils engage in this process of problem posing is another way of both assessing them and bringing them to terms with the overall process of solving problems.

Building a problem-solving process

The cyclical model *Analyse–Explore–Try* provides a very helpful means of organising and discussing possible solutions. However, care must be taken that it is not seen simply as a procedure to be memorised and then applied in a routine manner to every new problem. Rather, it needs to be carefully developed over a range of different problems, highlighting the components that are developed with each new problem.

Analyse

- As pupils read a problem, the need to first read for the *meaning* of the problem can be stressed. This may require reading more than once and can be helped by asking pupils to state in their own words what the problem is asking them to do.

- Further reading will be needed to sort out which information is needed and whether some is not needed or if other information needs to be gathered from the problem's context (e.g. data presented within the illustration or table accompanying the problem), or whether the pupils' mathematical understandings need to be used to find other relationships among the information. As the form of the problems becomes more complex, this thinking will be extended to incorporate further ways of dealing with the information; for example, measurement units, fractions and larger numbers might need to be renamed to the same mathematical form.

- Thinking about any processes that might be needed and the order in which they are used, as well as the type of answer that could occur, should also be developed in the context of new levels of problem structure.

- Developing a capacity to see 'through' the problem's expression—or context to see similarities between new problems and others that might already have been met—is a critical way of building expertise in coming to terms with and solving problems.

Explore

- When a problem is being explored, some problems will require the use of materials to think through the whole of the problem's context. Others will demand the use of diagrams to show what is needed. Another will show how systematic analysis of the situation using a sequence of diagrams, on a list or table, is helpful. As these ways of thinking about the problem are understood, they can be included in the cycle of steps.

Try

- Many pupils often try to guess a result. This can even be encouraged by talking about 'guess and check' as a means to solve problems. Changing to 'try and adjust' is more helpful in building a way of thinking and can lead to a very powerful way of finding solutions.

Expanding the problem-solving process

- Put the solution back into the problem.
- Does the answer make sense?
- Does it solve the problem?
- Is it the only answer?
- Could there be another way?

Analyse the problem

- Read carefully.
- What is the problem asking?
- What is the meaning of the information? Is it all needed? Is there too little? Too much?
- Which operations will be needed and in what order?
- What sort of answer is likely?
- Have I seen a problem like this before?

Try a solution strategy

- Use materials or a model.
- Use a calculator.
- Use pencil and paper.
- Look for a pattern.

Explore means to a solution

- Use a diagram or materials.
- Work backwards or backtrack.
- Put the information into a table.
- Try and adjust.

- When materials, a diagram or table have been used, another means to a solution is to look for a pattern in the results. When these have revealed what is needed to try for a solution, it may also be reasonable to use pencil and paper or a calculator.

Analyse

- The point in the cycle where an answer is assessed for reasonableness (e.g. whether it provides a solution, is only one of several solutions or whether there may be another way to solve the problem) also needs to be brought to the fore as different problems are met.

The role of calculators

When calculators are used, pupils devote less time to basic calculations, providing time that might be needed to either explore a solution or find an answer to a problem. In this way, attention is shifted from computation, which the calculator can do, to thinking about the problem and its solution—work that the calculator cannot do. It also allows more problems (and more realistic problems) to be addressed in problem-solving sessions. In these situations, a calculator serves as a tool rather than a crutch, requiring pupils to think through the problem's solution in order to know how to use the calculator appropriately. It also underpins the need to make sense of the steps along the way and any answers that result, as keying incorrect numbers, operations or order of operations quickly leads to results that are not appropriate.

Choosing, adapting and extending problems

When problems are selected, they need to be examined to see if pupils already have an understanding of the underlying mathematics required and that the problem's expression can be meaningfully read by the group of pupils who will be attempting the solution—though not necessarily by *all* pupils in the group. The problem itself should be neither too easy (so that it is just an exercise, repeating something readily done before), nor too difficult (thus beyond the capabilities of most or all in the group). A problem should engage the interests of the pupils and also be able to be solved in more than one way.

As a problem and its solution is reviewed, posing similar questions—where the numbers, shapes or measurements are changed—focuses attention back on what was entailed in analysing the problem and in exploring the means to a solution. Extending these processes to more complex situations shows how the particular approach can be extended to other situations and how patterns can be analysed to obtain more general methods or results. It also highlights the importance of a systematic approach when conceiving and discussing a solution and can lead to pupils asking themselves further questions about the situation and pose problems of their own as the significance of the problem's structure is uncovered.

Problem structure and expression

When analysing a problem, it is also possible to discern critical aspects of the problem's form and relate this to an appropriate level of mathematics and problem expression when choosing or extending problems. A problem of first-level complexity uses simple mathematics and simple language. A second-level problem may have simple language and more difficult mathematics or more difficult language and simple mathematics, while a third-level problem has yet more difficult language and mathematics. Within a problem, the processes that must be used may be more or less obvious, the information that is required for a solution may be too much or too little, and strategic thinking may be needed in order to come to terms with what the problem is asking.

Level	processes obvious	processes less obvious	too much information	too little information	strategic thinking
increasing difficulty with problem's expression and mathematics required	simple expression, simple mathematics				
	more complex expression, simple mathematics				
	simple expression, more complex mathematics				
	complex expression, complex mathematics				

The varying levels of problem structure and expression

(i) The processes to be used are relatively obvious, as these problems are comparatively straightforward and contain all the information necessary to find a solution.

(ii) The processes required are not immediately obvious, as these problems contain all the information necessary to find a solution but demand further analysis to sort out what is wanted and pupils may need to reverse what initially seemed to be required.

(iii) The problem contains more information than is needed for a solution, as these problems contain not only all the information needed to find a solution but also additional information in the form of times, numbers, shapes or measurements.

(iv) Further information must be gathered and applied to the problem in order to obtain a solution. These problems do not contain all the information necessary to find a solution but do contain a means to obtain the required information. The problem's setting, the pupil's mathematical understanding or the problem's wording need to be searched for the additional material.

(v) Strategic thinking is required to analyse the question in order to determine a solution strategy. Deeper analysis, often aided by the use of diagrams or tables, is needed to come to terms with what the problem is asking so a means to a solution can be determined.

This analysis of the nature of problems can also serve as a means of evaluating the provision of problems within a mathematics programme. In particular, it can lead to the development of a full range of problems, ensuring they are included across all problem forms, with the mathematics and expression suited to the level of the pupils.

Assessing problem-solving

Assessment of problem-solving requires careful and close observation of pupils working in a problem-solving setting. These observations can reveal the range of problem forms and the level of complexity in the expression and underlying mathematics that a pupil is able to confidently deal with. Further analysis of these observations can show to what extent the pupil is able to analyse the question, explore ways to a solution, select one or more methods to try and then analyse any results obtained. It is the combination of two fundamental aspects—the types of problem that can be solved and the manner in which solutions are carried out—that will give a measure of a pupil's developing problem-solving abilities, rather than a one-off test in which some problems are solved and others are not.

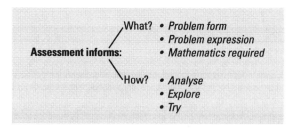

Assessment informs:

What? • *Problem form*
• *Problem expression*
• *Mathematics required*

How? • *Analyse*
• *Explore*
• *Try*

Observations based on this analysis have led to a categorisation of many of the possible difficulties that pupils experience with problem-solving as a whole, rather than the misconceptions they may have about particular problems. These often involve inappropriate attempts at a solution based on little understanding of the problem.

A major cause of possible difficulties is the *lack of a well-developed plan* of attack, leading pupils to focus on the *surface level* of problems. In such cases, pupils:

- locate and manipulate numbers with little or no thought about their relevance to the problem
- try a succession of different operations if the first ones attempted do not yield a (likely) result
- focus on keywords for an indication of what might be done without considering their significance within the problem as a whole
- read problems quickly and cursorily to locate the numbers to be used

xviii
Problem-solving in mathematics
www.prim-ed.com   Prim-Ed Publishing®

Problem	Likely causes
Pupil is unable to make any attempt at a solution.	• not interested • feels overwhelmed • cannot think of how to start to answer question • needs to reconsider complexity of steps and information
Pupil has no means of linking the situation to the implicit mathematical meaning.	• needs to create diagram or use materials • needs to consider separate parts of question and then bring parts together
Pupil uses an inappropriate operation.	• misled by word cues or numbers • has underdeveloped concepts • uses rote procedures rather than real understanding
Pupil is unable to translate a problem into a more familiar process.	• cannot see interactions between operations • lack of understanding means he/she unable to reverse situations • data may need to be used in an order not evident in the problem statement or in an order contrary to that in which it is presented

• use the first available word cue to suggest the operation that might be needed.

Other possible difficulties result from a focus on being quick, which leads to:

• no attempt to assess the reasonableness of an answer

• little perseverance if an answer is not obtained using the first approach tried

• not being able to access strategies to which they have been introduced.

When the approaches to problem processing developed in this series are followed and the specific suggestions for solving particular problems or types of problems are discussed with pupils, these difficulties can be minimised, if not entirely avoided. Analysing the problem before starting leads to an understanding of the problem's meanings. The cycle of steps within the model means that nothing is tried before the intent of the problem is clear and the means to a solution have been considered. Focusing on a problem's meaning and discussing what needs to be done builds perseverance. Making sense of the steps that must be followed and any answers that result are central to the problem-solving process. These difficulties are unlikely to occur among those who have built up an understanding of this way of thinking.

A final comment

If an approach to problem-solving can be built up using the ideas developed here and the problems in the investigations on the pages that follow, pupils will develop a way of thinking about and with mathematics that will allow them to readily solve problems and generalise from what they already know to understand new mathematical ideas. They will engage with these emerging mathematical conceptions from their very beginnings, be prepared to debate and discuss their own ideas, and develop attitudes that will allow them to tackle new problems and topics. Mathematics can then be a subject that is readily engaged with and can become one in which the pupil feels in control, instead of one in which many rules devoid of meaning have to be memorised and applied at the right time. This early enthusiasm for learning and the ability to think mathematically will lead to a search for meaning in new situations and processes that will allow mathematical ideas to be used across a range of applications in school and everyday life.

Problem-solving

To use spatial visualisation and logical reasoning to solve problems.

Curriculum links

England (Year 3)
- Using and applying: Identify patterns and relationships involving shapes and use these to solve problems.

Northern Ireland (Key Stage 1)
- Processes in maths: Develop different approaches to problem solving.
- Processes in maths: Recognise simple patterns and relationships.
- Shape and space: Make patterns using 2-D shapes.

Scotland (First)
- Patterns and relationships: Continue and devise repeating patterns.
- Patterns and relationships: Explore simple 2-D shapes and how different shapes fit together.

Wales (Key Stage 2)
- Skills: Select and use the appropriate mathematics to solve problems in a variety of contexts.
- Skills: Recognise, and generalise in words, patterns that arise in spatial situations.

Materials

Square grid paper, blocks or squares in five different colours

Focus

These pages explore possible arrangements of shapes or combinations of coloured squares on a grid in order to determine how a particular outcome can be formed. Spatial as well as logical thinking and organisation are involved as pupils investigate all likely arrangements to ensure the final forms match the given criteria.

Discussion

Page 3

Pupils will need to physically manipulate the shapes in order to see the pattern involved in extending each shape. The first shape replicates the manner in which the larger square was constructed. The triangles require one of the pieces to be flipped in order to make the larger triangle. Encourage pupils to continue the patterns to make the next largest shape.

Page 4

The grids can be organised in a number of ways. However, each different way will have one or two diagonals with four blocks of the same colour. Two grids are provided to enable pupils to explore and try different possible arrangements.

Page 5

This activity builds on and extends the pupils' previous experience of the 4-by-4 grid by extending the grid to 5-by-5 and by introducing an additional colour. Again, the grid can be organised in a number of ways. Pupils should be encouraged to explore and try different possible arrangements.

Possible difficulties

- Not rotating or flipping shapes to eliminate duplicates or to 'grow' a shape
- Inability to visualise the pattern needed to grow a shape
- Not considering both rows and columns

Extension

- Investigate growing other shapes using different numbers of squares or shapes.
- Extend the grid to 6-by-6 and use six different colours.
- Explore other shapes that can be made using four of Shape 1.
- Investigate making these shapes using Shape 3.

Four squares can make a larger square.

Use four of each of these shapes to make a larger copy of the shape.
Draw the new shape you made.

Shape 1

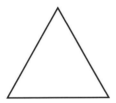

Shape 2

Shape 3

Take four blocks of four different colours (16 blocks).

Place blocks on the grid so that no row or column has the same colour in it.

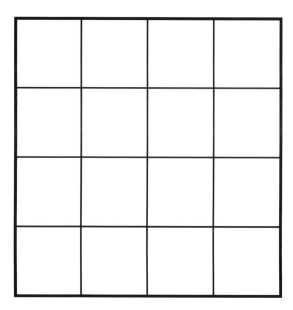

What do you notice? _____

Try doing it a different way.

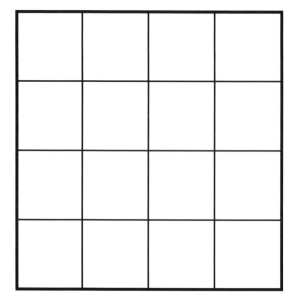

GRID FUN 2

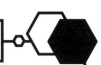

Take five blocks of five different colours (25 blocks).

1. Place the blocks on the grid so that no row or column has the same colour in it.

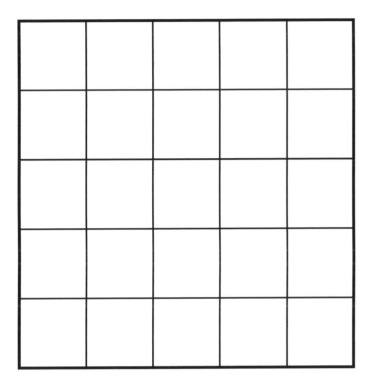

What do you notice? _____

Try doing it a different way.

Problem-solving

To use strategic thinking to solve problems.

Curriculum links

England (Year 3)

- Using and applying: Solve one-step and two-step problems involving numbers, choosing and carrying out appropriate calculations.
- Using and applying: Present the information in a problem using diagrams and use these to find a solution.

Northern Ireland (Key Stage 1)

- Processes in maths: Develop different approaches to problem solving.

Scotland (First)

- +/-/x/÷: Use operations when solving problems, making the best use of mental strategies and written skills developed.

Wales (Key Stage 2)

- Skills: Select and use the appropriate mathematics to solve problems in a variety of contexts.

Materials

12 counters (1 one colour, 11 another colour)

Focus

This page introduces a more complex problem in which the most difficult step is to try and find a way of understanding the question and what it is asking. Using materials to explore the problem is one way this can be done. Another is to use a diagram to assist in 'thinking backwards' by trying and adjusting possible answers until a solution that matches all of the conditions is found.

Discussion

Page 7

The problems can be solved in several ways. One is to work backwards from the final position, reasoning that the reverse of each condition must be performed—for example, that Gina finishes in fourth position and must pass three cars and then be passed by seven cars to get back to her original position.

Some pupils may need counters to model the process of cars passing and being passed. Pupils could use the 12 counters, with the single-colour counter representing Gina's car, and the other counters (of a second colour) representing the other 11 cars. Other pupils may prefer to base their solution on a diagram that shows what has happened.

Also, rather than working backwards, some pupils may prefer to work forwards; choosing a position for Gina and working through each of the events in the race. If Gina does not end up in fourth place, an adjustment will need to be made to the original position chosen. In this way, a process of 'try and adjust' can lead to the correct starting position. Note that the positive expression 'try and adjust' is much more helpful than the often used 'guess and check'.

The second problem extends the concept; however, this time the initial position is given and the question is reversed so that pupils are asked for the number of cars that Jordan needs to pass to take the winning position.

Possible difficulties

- Using only the seven cars that Gina passed to determine her starting position
- Using only the three cars that passed Gina to determine her starting position
- Thinking only of the three cars between Jordan's starting position and first place
- Thinking that Jordan needs to pass 10 cars, when being in tenth position means he has to pass nine cars to win

Extension

- Pupils write their own car race problems based on these questions.
- Use a different context rather than racing cars for the stories.

At the start of a car race, the cars line up in their starting positions.

1. Gina is driving one of the 12 cars in the race. During the race, she passes seven cars before being passed by three cars. She finishes the race in fourth place.

   In what position did Gina start the race?

   _____

2. Jordan started in fourth place. During the race, he was passed by six cars.

   How many cars does he need to pass to win the race?

   _____

Problem-solving

To read, interpret and analyse information.

Curriculum links

England (Year 3)
- Using and applying: Solve one-step and two-step problems involving numbers, choosing and carrying out appropriate calculations.
- Counting and understanding whole number: Order whole numbers.

Northern Ireland (Key Stage 1)
- Processes in maths: Develop different approaches to problem solving.
- Number: Order whole numbers and understand that the place value of the digit indicates its value.

Scotland (First)
- Number processes: Know the link between a digit, its place and its value.
- +/-/x/÷: Use operations when solving problems, making the best use of mental strategies and written skills developed.

Wales (Key Stage 2)
- Skills: Select and use the appropriate mathematics to solve problems in a variety of contexts.
- Skills: Identify and process the information needed to carry out work.
- Number: Order whole numbers and understand place value in relation to the position of digits.

Materials

Some pupils may need counters or number expanders.

Focus

These pages explore relationships among numbers and then use this analysis to find a number that matches specific criteria. This process encourages pupils to disregard numbers that are not possible rather than simply looking for ones that are likely to work. When placing the numbers in the problem situations, pupils need to read the stories carefully in order to work out what number goes where.

Discussion

Page 9
Some pupils will use the listed information to discard numbers until only the correct number remains, while other pupils may prefer to try each number in turn against all of the criteria until they find a number that answers all conditions. The criteria listed allow numbers to be selected as well as ruled out; for example, 'less than 76 tens' rules out 763, 776 and 795.

Some pupils may work down the list of conditions, while others may read all the conditions and then decide where to start. This concept has been extended by having pupils think of their own number and write specific criteria for others to identify it.

Page 10
These problems require pupils to read and interpret the problem situations and then arrange the numbers that are provided so that the resulting stories make sense. The numbers are not listed in the order in which they are used in the stories. This concept has been extended by having pupils think of their own stories/problems and include the numbers to solve the problems.

Page 11
Careful analysis of each problem is needed to take into consideration the use of a number of mathematics terms; for example: twice, half, 'in three years time'. Some problems require pupils to start with the age listed at the end of the problem and then 'backtrack' in order to find a solution. If needed, materials such as counters can be used to assist.

Possible difficulties

- Selecting a number that matches only the first criterion
- Not matching the number against all criteria
- Not considering terms such as 'twice' and 'half'

Extension

- Pupils think of a number and make up criteria to match it, then give it to other pupils to solve.
- Pupils can be encouraged to come up with mathematical criteria of their own rather than using just the same criteria listed.

My number ...

| 763 | 776 | 729 | 757 | 739 | 795 |

- is between 69 tens and 79 tens
- is more than 73 tens
- has 7 in the hundreds place
- does not have 3 in the ones place
- is less than 76 tens
- has a digit larger than 8 in the ones place.

1. My number is _____.

My number ...

| 356 | 563 | 653 | 536 | 635 | 365 |

- is between 30 tens and 60 tens
- is less than 57 tens
- uses the digits 3, 5, 6
- does not have 3 in the hundreds place
- has a digit larger than 5 in the ones place.

2.   My number is _____.

3. Make up your own number puzzle and give it to a friend to solve.

My number is ...

_____   _____

_____   _____

_____   _____

MISSING NUMBERS

Some numbers have been left out of the stories below. Put in the numbers so the stories make sense.

4	43	8	5	10

1. Jake's mother drives to work. She leaves at _____ o'clock in the morning. She stops work at _____ o'clock and collects Jake from after-school care. They arrive home at about _____ o'clock. She is _____ years old. Jake is _____ years old.

6	5	8	10	1

Joseph, Jacob and Jonathan are brothers. Joseph is older than Jonathan. Jonathan is older than Jacob. Jonathan is in Year 4 at school.

2. Record the age and year level of each boy.

	Joseph	Jacob	Jonathan
Age			
Year level			4

3. Write your own 'missing numbers' story and give it to a friend to solve.

_____

_____

_____

_____

_____

WHAT'S MY AGE?

1. 'My sister is twice my age. She will be 15 next year.

   'How old am I?' _____

2. 'I am five years younger than my brother. I will be 12 next year.

   'How old is he?' _____

3. 'My cousin is three times my age. She was 14 last year.

   'How old am I?' _____

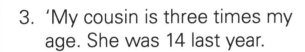

4. 'My older brother will be 16 in four years time. I am half his age.

   'How old am I now?'_____

5. 'My cousin is twice my age. She was 11 last year.

   'How old am I?' _____

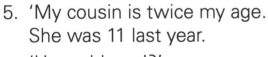

6. 'I will be nine in three years time. My sister is twice my age.

   'How old is she?' _____

7. 'My little sister is six. I will be twice her age in three years time.

   'How old am I now?' _____

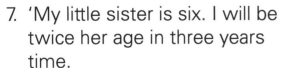

Prim-Ed Publishing®   www.prim-ed.com   Problem-solving in mathematics

Problem-solving

To analyse and use information word problems.

Curriculum links

England (Year 3)

- Using and applying: Solve one-step and two-step problems involving numbers, choosing and carrying out appropriate calculations.
- Calculating: Add and subtract mentally.
- Calculating: Use written methods to add, subtract and multiply.

Northern Ireland (Key Stage 1)

- Processes in maths: Select the mathematics appropriate for a task.
- Processes in maths: Develop different approaches to problem solving.
- Number: Understand the operations of addition, subtraction and multiplication, and use them to solve problems.
- Number: Know addition, subtraction and multiplication facts.
- Number: Develop strategies for adding and subtracting mentally.

Scotland (First)

- +/-/x/÷: Use addition, subtraction and multiplication when solving problems, making best use of mental strategies and written skills developed.

Wales (Key Stage 2)

- Skills: Select and use the appropriate mathematics to solve problems in a variety of contexts.
- Skills: Identify and process the information needed to carry out work.
- Number: Use a variety of mental methods of computation and extend written methods.

Materials

Place value chart, calculator

Focus

These pages explore word problems that require addition, subtraction or multiplication. Pupils need to determine what the problem is asking and, in many cases, carry out more than one step in order to find the solution. Analysis of the problems reveals that unlike items may need to be added, which is more complex than just adding two or more like items together, while other problems contain additional information that is not needed.

If necessary, materials can be used to assist with the calculation, since these problems are about reading for information and determining what the problem is asking rather than just computation or basic facts.

Discussion

Page 13

These problems require more than one step and may involve addition as well as subtraction. The wording has been kept simple to assist with the problem-solving process. Pupils may choose a number of different ways to find a solution. For example, in the second problem, the people who go swimming (8) and walking (7) could be added together and then subtracted from the total of 42; or, alternatively, 8 could be subtracted from 42 and then 7 subtracted from 34 to obtain a solution. Pupils should be encouraged to try different ways of arriving at a solution.

Page 14

A careful reading of each question is needed to determine what the problem is asking. In some cases, there is more information than needed and each problem contains numbers that are not required to find a solution. Some problems require more than one step and both addition and subtraction are needed at times. Again, there are a number of ways to find a solution and pupils should be encouraged to explore and try different possibilities of arriving at an answer.

Page 15

Most of these problems require multiplication, so the wording and the steps involved have been kept fairly simple. Pupils may find it helpful to draw a diagram to work out what is happening in the problem and to determine what needs to be multiplied to find a solution. Addition can be used at times rather than multiplication.

Possible difficulties

- Inability to identify the need to add, subtract or multiply
- Confusion over the need to carry out more than one step or type of calculation to arrive at a solution
- Using all the numbers listed in the problem rather than just the numbers needed

Extension

- Pupils could write their own problems and give them to other pupils to solve.

AT THE BEACH

1. 38 people are swimming in the sea.
   Nine more people get in, but 13 get out. How many people are now swimming in the sea?

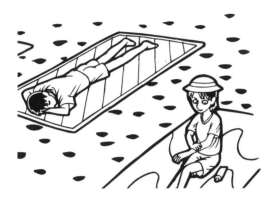

2. 42 people are lying on their towels. Eight people get up for a swim and seven people leave for a walk. How many people are still lying on their towels?

3. 39 surfers are on their boards waiting for waves. 21 more surfers arrive, but nine get out. How many surfers are now waiting for waves?

4. 47 people are swimming between the flags. 14 more arrive, but some get out. If there are now 42 people swimming, how many got out?

5. 27 surfers are trying to catch waves. If only 16 surfers catch a wave, how many did not catch the wave?

AT THE PARTY

1. There are 37 people at the party. On one table there are 43 sausage rolls and on another table there are 39 sausage rolls. How many sausage rolls are there altogether?

   _____

2. There are 58 party pies on one tray and 46 party pies on another tray. During the party, 18 people eat 34 of the party pies. How many party pies were not eaten?

   _____

3. There are 20 spring rolls and 30 meatballs on one tray and 30 spring rolls and 40 meatballs on another tray. 37 meatballs and 42 spring rolls are eaten. How many more meatballs than spring rolls are left?

   _____

4. There are 56 soft drinks and 59 juice drinks on one table and 35 soft drinks and 25 juice drinks on another table. During the party, people drank 39 soft drinks and 43 juice drinks.

   (a) How many soft drinks are left? _____

   (b) How many drinks were drunk? _____

IN THE GARDEN

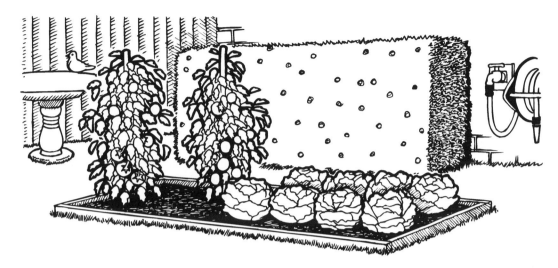

1. Fran planted 29 rows of tomatoes. Each row has 9 plants. How many tomato plants did she plant?

    _____

2. Fran watered 4 rows of lettuces in the morning and 6 rows in the afternoon. Each row has 15 lettuces. How many lettuces were watered?

    _____

3. Fran picked some tomatoes and packed them in trays. Each tray holds 6 tomatoes. She filled 18 trays and had 4 tomatoes left over. How many tomatoes did she pick?

    _____

4. Fran picked 3 rows of lettuces each day for 4 days. Each row has 15 lettuces. How many lettuces did she pick?

    _____

5. Fran wants to sell 4 boxes of lettuces at the market. Each box holds 24 lettuces. How many lettuces does she need to pack to fill her boxes?

    _____

6. Fran picked 36 tomatoes and 48 lettuces in the morning and 56 tomatoes and 35 lettuces in the afternoon. How many tomatoes did she pick?

    _____

Problem-solving
To use strategic thinking to solve problems.

Curriculum links
England (Year 3)
- Using and applying: Identify patterns and relationships involving numbers and use these to solve problems.

Northern Ireland (Key Stage 1)
- Processes in maths: Develop different approaches to problem solving.
- Processes in maths: Organise their own work and work systematically.
- Processes in maths: Recognise simple patterns and relationships.

Scotland (First)
- Patterns and relationships: Explore number patterns.

Wales (Key Stage 2)
- Skills: Select and use the appropriate mathematics to solve problems in a variety of contexts.
- Skills: Recognise, and generalise in words, patterns that arise in numerical situations.

Materials

0–99 number board

0	1	2	3	4	5	6	7	8	9
10	11	12	13	14	15	16	17	18	19
20	21	22	23	24	25	26	27	28	29
30	31	32	33	34	35	36	37	38	39
40	41	42	43	44	45	46	47	48	49
50	51	52	53	54	55	56	57	58	59
60	61	62	63	64	65	66	67	68	69
70	71	72	73	74	75	76	77	78	79
80	81	82	83	84	85	86	87	88	89
90	91	92	93	94	95	96	97	98	99

Focus
This page explores pupils' understanding of the number system and their ability to solve questions about numbers. Pupils need to coordinate the reading and writing of numerals with the symbols involved in writing the numbers 0–99.

Discussion
Page 17

These investigations explore pupils' ability to solve questions about the number system and to keep track of the possible answers they find. In coming to terms with the question, they must discuss what it means to *say* a digit as opposed to *writing* it. As the problems progress

to exploring other numbers, there will be further aspects to consider, such as how '3' or '5' is read in some numbers and how the 'four' in 'fourteen' and 'forty' sound the same even when written differently.

For the first question, pupils must realise that 'one' is said nine times from 0–99 in the ones place for 1, 21, 31… but not for 'eleven'. There will be another nine of the same form from 100–199, together with the 100 times 'one' is said with each 'one hundred and …'. 'One' is said a total of 118 times. If pupils need help in organising their solution, they can write or be given a 0–99 board that shows how place value uses tens and ones for two-digit numbers. However, they should be left to explore their own ways of coming to terms with the problem and determining solutions, rather than simply replacing it with an exercise in counting every '1' in the 0–99 board. The digit '1' is written 140 times. Careful consideration must be given to 11 and 111 to see this.

For the second question, 'two' is also said nine times from 0–99, with another nine times from 100–199 and another for '200'. From 1–200, the digit '2' is written 41 times.

If pupils take the problem further and try other one-digit numbers, as suggested, they will find that 'three' has a similar pattern as 'two'. However, there is a different pattern altogether when saying 'four'. For this to occur, you have to include the pronunciation of the word part 'four' within 'fourteen', 'forty', 'forty-one' etc. The pattern repeats for the digits 6 to 9 (with the pronunciation, for example, of 'six' within 'sixty'). When pupils notice this they will have really come to terms with the strategic thinking needed to organise and solve problems with several interacting conditions.

Possible difficulties
- Unable to keep track of the number of times they determine a digit or word
- Confusion between saying and writing the digits
- Confusion with 11 and 22 and only seeing the digits '1' and '2' once when they actually occur in both the ones and tens place

Extension
- Make a table for the pupils to display their results and present a description of the problems and their solutions to another class or group.

HOW MANY DIGITS?

1. (a) When you count from one to two hundred, how many times do you say 'one'?

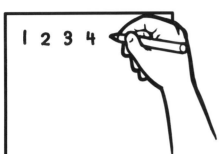

One, two, three ...

(b) How many times would you write '1' if you were to write all of the numbers from 1 to 200?

_____

One hundred and one, one hundred and two ...

2. (a) When counting from one to two hundred, do you think you would you say 'two' more, the same, or less times than you would say 'one'?

_____

(b) How many times would you say 'two'?

_____

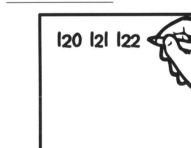

(c) How many times would you write '2' when writing the numbers from 1 to 200?

_____

3. Try other 1-digit numbers. Can you see any patterns?

_____

_____

_____

Problem-solving

To develop spatial visualisation in order to solve problems and build a means of organising information in more complex problems.

Curriculum links

England (Year 3)
- Using and applying: Identify patterns and relationships involving shapes and use these to solve problems.
- Understanding shape: Visualise and make 2-D shapes.

Northern Ireland (Key Stage 1)
- Processes in maths: Develop different approaches to problem solving.
- Shape and space: Make pictures using 2-D shapes.

Scotland (First)
- Patterns and relationships: Continue and devise repeating patterns.
- Properties of 2-D shapes: Explore simple 2-D shapes and how different shapes fit together.

Wales (Key Stage 2)
- Skills: Select and use the appropriate mathematics to solve problems in a variety of contexts.
- Skills: Recognise patterns that arise in spatial situations.
- Shape, position and movement: Make 2-D shapes and patterns.

Materials

Tangram puzzles made from the template on page 56

Focus

These pages explore the use of tangrams to make shapes as well as the arrangement of shapes. Spatial and logical thinking and organisation are involved, as pupils investigate manipulating the pieces to make the various shapes. Being able to visualise in this way will assist pupils in solving many other problems in number, measurement, and chance and data, as well other spatial problems.

Point out to pupils that the shapes on the worksheets are not to scale with the tangram pieces.

Discussion

Page 19

These activities are designed for pupils to explore the relative sizes of the individual pieces and the ways they can fit together to make readily identifiable shapes. As a starting point some of the tangram pieces used have been drawn and identified, leaving the pupils to work out the arrangement of the other pieces to complete the shapes.

Page 20

Building on the experiences gained from the previous page, the pupils' understanding is extended to explore the relative sizes of the individual pieces and the ways they can fit together to make geometric shapes. Again, some of the pieces used have been drawn and identified, leaving the pupils to work out the arrangement of the other pieces to complete the shapes.

Page 21

This page challenges pupils to explore the relative sizes of the individual pieces and the ways they can fit together to make more abstract shapes. Again, some of the pieces used have been drawn and identified, leaving the pupils to work out the arrangement of the other pieces to complete the shapes.

Possible difficulties

- Not readily rotating and/or flipping pieces to complete the shapes

Extension

- How many small triangles are needed to make the square, medium and large triangles?
- What about the other shape (a parallelogram)?
- Pupils can investigate other tangram shapes by using various Prim-Ed Publishing books or by searching the Internet.

Cut out the pieces of the tangram from the sheet your teacher gives you. Use them to make the following shapes.

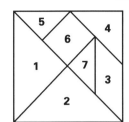

1. Use all of the pieces to make the bird. Three of the pieces are shown.

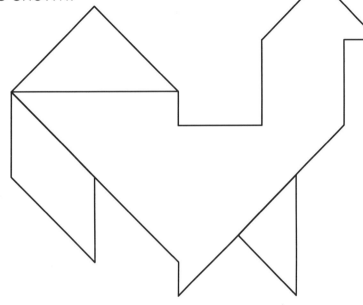

2. Use all of the pieces to make the bird. Two of the pieces are shown.

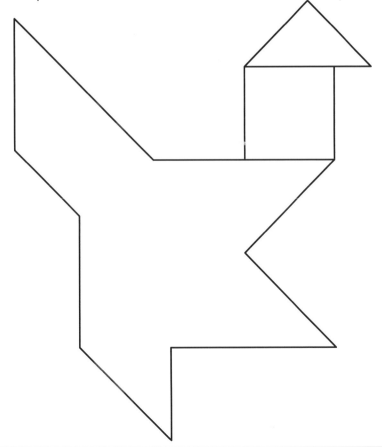

Cut out the pieces of the tangram from the sheet your teacher gives you. Use them to make the following shapes.

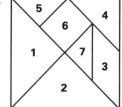

1. Use all of the pieces to make the shape. Three of the pieces are shown.

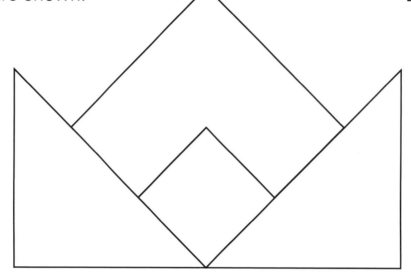

2. Use all of the pieces to make the shape. Two of the pieces are shown.

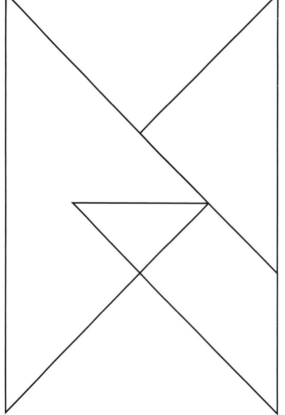

Draw lines to show how you placed the rest of the pieces.

TANGRAMS 3

Cut out the pieces of the tangram from the sheet your teacher gives you. Use them to make the following shapes.

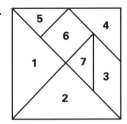

1. Use all of the pieces to make the shape. Two of the pieces are shown.

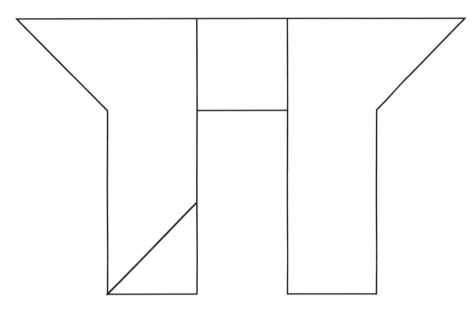

2. This shape has a hole in the middle. Use all of the pieces to make the shape. One piece is shown.

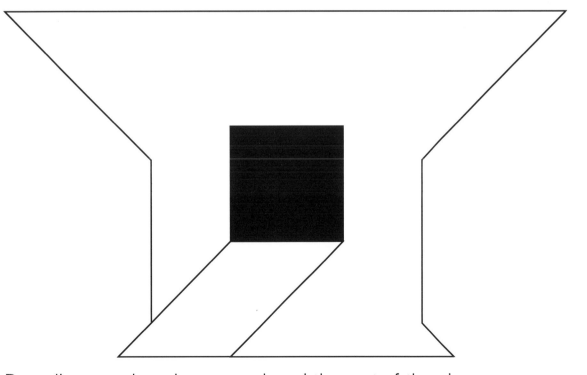

Draw lines to show how you placed the rest of the pieces.

Problem-solving

Use the concept of magic squares.

Curriculum links

England (Year 3)

- Using and applying: Solve problems involving numbers, choosing and carrying out appropriate calculations.
- Calculating: Add mentally.

Northern Ireland (Key Stage 1)

- Processes in maths: Develop different approaches to problem solving.
- Number: Understand the operation of addition, and use it to solve problems.
- Number: Know addition facts.
- Number: Develop strategies for adding mentally.

Scotland (First)

- +/-/x/÷: Use addition when solving problems, making best use of mental strategies developed.

Wales (Key Stage 2)

- Skills: Solve problems in a variety of contexts.
- Number: Use a variety of mental methods of computation.

Materials

Blocks, calculator

Focus

These pages explore the properties of magic squares and other shapes. Pupils must analyse the problems and locate the information necessary to find each magic number. With each square, once the magic number is known, it is then possible to proceed to find the missing numbers.

Counters, blocks or a calculator can be used by pupils to assist them, as the focus is the concept of magic squares and magic numbers rather than addition, subtraction or basic facts.

Discussion

Page 23

This investigation introduces the concept of magic squares. Simple 3-by-3 magic squares are used to help pupils to come to understand the idea that each row, column and diagonal adds to the same magic number.

Page 24

This page continues the previous concept. Again, simple 3-by-3 magic squares are used to help pupils understand the idea that each row, column and diagonal adds to the same magic number. In this case, pupils investigate what happens to a magic square if they add one or three to each number in the square.

Page 25

In this situation, shapes other than squares are investigated. The first examples, using the digits one to six, involve triangles, with each side of each triangle adding to make a magic number. The problems that follow involve more complex shapes, with four and five numbers in each of the lines adding to the same magic number.

Possible difficulty

- Considering only rows or columns rather than rows, columns and diagonals

Extension

- Discuss all possibilities the pupils discover for the magic shapes—are they really different from each other?
- Investigate other magic squares and magic numbers.

Magic squares have rows, columns and diagonals that all add to the same magic number.

7	0	5
2	4	6
3	8	1

1. This magic square has a magic number of _____.

2. Complete the magic squares. Remember, all rows, columns and diagonals must add to the same magic number.

Under each magic square, write the magic number.

(a)

8	1	6
	5	

(b)

11		9
	8	
		5

(c)

32	4	24
16		8

(d)

4		8
	7	
6		

MAGIC SQUARES 2

Complete the magic squares. Remember that all rows, columns and diagonals must add to the same magic number.

1. The magic number is under each magic square.

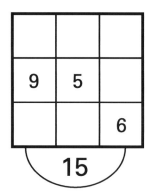

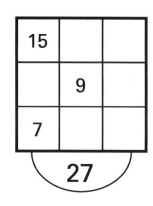

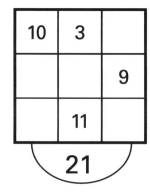

2. What happens if you add one to each number in the above magic squares?

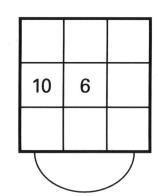

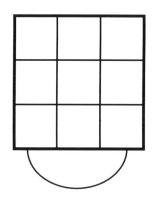

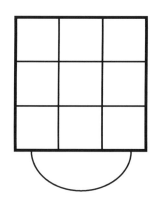

Are they still magic squares? _____

3. What happens if you add three to each number?

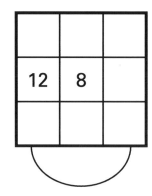

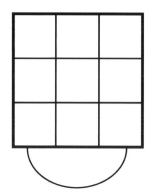

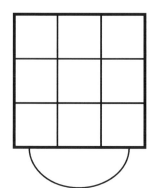

Are they still magic squares? _____

MAGIC CIRCLES

Use the digits from one to six to make each side or line add to the same total.

1. Write the magic number under each shape.

(a)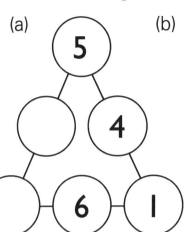

(b)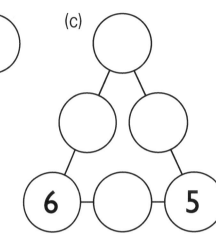

(c)

_____   _____   _____

2. Now try these magic shapes, using the digits from one to nine. The magic number is written under each shape.

(a)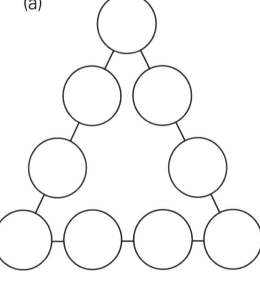

(b)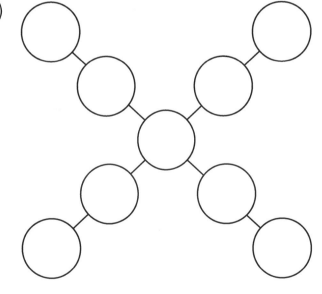

21

27

(c) Is there more than one way to arrange the numbers? _____

Problem-solving

To solve problems involving money and make decisions based on particular criteria.

Curriculum links

England (Year 3)
- Using and applying: Solve one-step and two-step problems involving money, choosing and carrying out appropriate calculations.
- Calculating: Add and subtract mentally.

Northern Ireland (Key Stage 1)
- Processes in maths: Select the mathematics appropriate for a task.
- Processes in maths: Develop different approaches to problem solving.
- Number: Understand the operations of addition, subtraction and multiplication, and use it to solve problems.
- Number: Know addition, subtraction and multiplication facts.
- Number: Develop strategies for adding and subtracting mentally.
- Number: Add and subtract money and solve money problems.

Scotland (First)
- +/-/x/÷: Use addition, subtraction and multiplication when solving problems, making best use of mental strategies developed.
- Money: Use money to pay for items and work out change.

Wales (Key Stage 2)
- Skills: Select and use the appropriate mathematics to solve problems in a variety of contexts.
- Skills: Identify and process the information needed to carry out work.
- Number: Use a variety of mental methods of computation.
- Measures and money: Use the (four) operations to solve problems involving money.

Materials

Some pupils may need counters, play money or a calculator.

Focus

This page explores the pupils' abilities to read for information, obtain information from another source (the tuckshop menu) and use it to find solutions. The problems are about using money, making decisions based on money and comparing amounts of money, rather than adding or subtracting. Solutions can be obtained by using materials and comparing amounts. Counters, blocks, play money or a calculator may be used if needed.

Discussion

Page 27

Pupils read the items on the menu and note how much each costs. The investigation involves pupils reading the questions for information as well as getting information from another source—the tuckshop menu.

Pupils need to remember what they are buying and then work out how much it costs and, in some cases, to add, subtract or compare amounts to see if they have enough money. The last two questions have a number of possible solutions. Some pupils might choose three items they would like and then add and compare only to discover they don't have enough money, while others might just choose the three cheapest items. Either way, they need to compare money amounts and make decisions accordingly.

Possible difficulties

- Unfamiliarity with the '£' symbol
- Not taking into account that they may need two or more of the same item
- Believing that the exact amount of £6 or £10 has to be spent as opposed to not spending all of the amount

Extension

- Record and discuss the different choices pupils make to spend their £10.
- In pairs, pupils write their own questions based on the tuckshop menu and give them to other pairs to solve.

TUCKSHOP

Sandwiches

Egg or cheese......................£1	
Tomato and cheese £2	
Ham or chicken....................£3	

Juice

Apple or orange....................£1
Lemon twist.......................£2

Rolls

Chicken or ham...................£4	
Salad £3	
Tomato and cheese £2	

Milk

Plain £1
Chocolate £2

1. Kelly has £5. Does she have enough to buy a ham sandwich and a chocolate milk?

   _____

2. Kurt has £9. Can he buy two chicken rolls and a lemon twist drink?

   _____

3. Kristy has £10. She buys a ham roll, a cheese sandwich and a plain milk. How much money does she have left?

   _____

4. Kerry bought three chocolate milks for her sisters. How much change does she have from £10?

   _____

5. Kwan has £6. He needs to buy lunch for himself and his two brothers. Choose what he can buy with his money.

   _____

6. If you had £10, what would you buy?

   _____

Problem-solving

To use spatial visualisation and logical reasoning to solve problems.

Curriculum links

England (Year 3)
- Using and applying: Identify patterns and relationships involving shapes and use these to solve problems.
- Understanding shape: Use the four compass directions to describe movement about a grid.

Northern Ireland (Key Stage 1)
- Processes in maths: Develop different approaches to problem solving.
- Processes in maths: Organise work and work systematically.
- Processes in maths: Recognise simple patterns and relationships.
- Shape and space: Know the four points of the compass.

Scotland (First)
- Patterns and relationships: Continue and devise repeating patterns.
- Angle: Follow routes using words associated with direction.

Wales (Key Stage 2)
- Skills: Select and use the appropriate mathematics to solve problems in a variety of contexts.
- Skills: Recognise patterns that arise in spatial situations.

Materials

Coloured pencils (red, green, blue and yellow), grid paper

Focus

These pages explore possible arrangements or combinations of objects in order to determine all possibilities in a situation. Spatial as well as logical thinking and organisation are involved as pupils investigate all likely arrangements and make sure that they do not repeat combinations. Acquiring the skill of systematic thinking needed to solve these problems will also solve many other problems, not merely those that involve similar arrangements.

Discussion

Page 29

The panes can be organised in the windows in 24 possible ways. With 25 panes drawn on the page, some pupils may simply repeat a previous combination in order to fill all of the panes. The problem states that they use one of each colour pane; therefore each window needs one red pane, one green pane, one blue pane and one yellow pane.

Page 30

This activity involves following directions and using coordinates. Pupils plot the path of a car, taking into account direction and distance. The first two grids are fairly simple, with just one journey in each direction. The next two grids involve moving back and forth in a number of different directions.

Page 31

This activity builds on and extends the experiences on page 29. Twenty possible designs can be made using six panes of glass in two different colours. As there are more windows than needed, some pupils may simply repeat a previous combination in order to fill all the panes. A systematic process of trying different combinations is needed to find all the possibilities and to avoid duplication.

Possible difficulties

- Not recognising that a design has been used more than once
- Using all of the windows, whether they were needed or not

Extension

- Discuss the methods that can be used to systematically find all of the possible designs.
- Use grid paper to investigate the possibilities of having five panes of glass with five different colours.

Tanya is fitting coloured glass into her window.

She has 1 red pane, 1 green pane, 1 blue pane and 1 yellow pane. Each time she makes a window, she uses one of each colour pane.

1. Colour the different designs can she make.

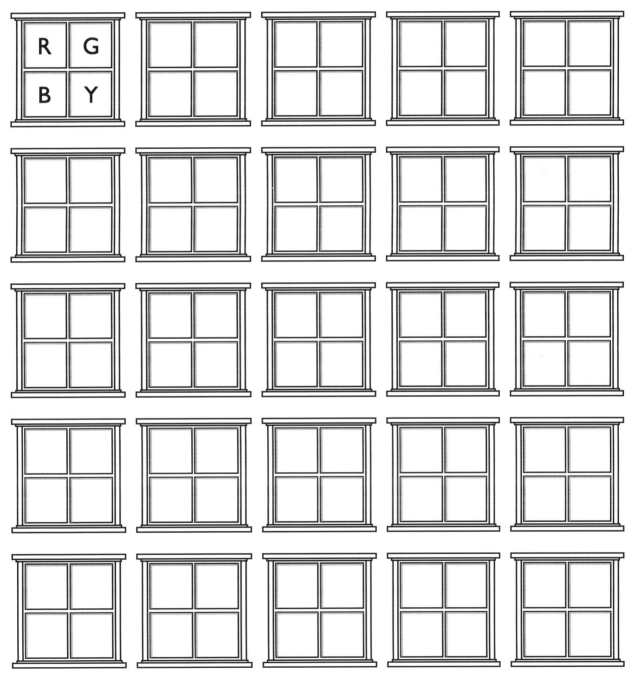

R	G
B	Y

2. How many different designs can she make? _____

DRIVE TIME

Draw the paths of the cars on the grids.

1.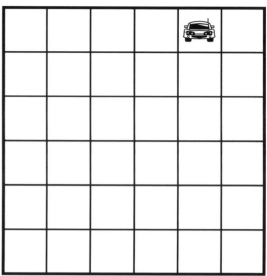

Drive

2 squares north
3 squares east
4 squares south
2 squares west

2.

Drive

5 squares south
3 squares west
4 squares north
2 squares west

3.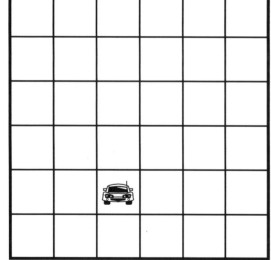

Drive

3 squares north
2 squares east
1 square north
1 square east
4 squares south
3 squares west

4.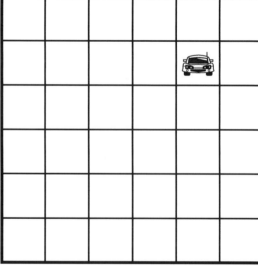

Drive

3 squares west
4 squares south
2 squares east
2 squares north
2 squares east
1 square north

Aisha is fitting coloured glass into her windows. For each window, she has 3 red panes and 3 blue panes.

1. Colour the different designs she can make. The first has been done for you.

R	R
R	B
B	B

2. How many different designs can she make? _____

Problem-solving

To analyse and determine information in written problems.

Curriculum links

England (Year 3)
- Using and applying: Solve one-step and two-step problems involving numbers, choosing and carrying out appropriate calculations.
- Calculating: Add and subtract mentally.
- Calculating: Use written methods to add, subtract and multiply.

Northern Ireland (Key Stage 1)
- Processes in maths: Select the mathematics appropriate for a task.
- Processes in maths: Develop different approaches to problem solving.
- Number: Understand the operations of addition, subtraction and multiplication, and use them to solve problems.
- Number: Know addition, subtraction and multiplication facts.
- Number: Develop strategies for adding and subtracting mentally.

Scotland (First)
- +/-/x/÷: Use addition, subtraction and multiplication when solving problems, making best use of mental strategies and written skills developed.

Wales (Key Stage 2)
- Skills: Select and use the appropriate mathematics to solve problems in a variety of contexts.
- Skills: Identify and process the information needed to carry out work.
- Number: Use a variety of mental methods of computation and extend written methods.

Materials

Place value chart, calculator

Focus

These pages explore problems that require addition, subtraction and multiplication. Pupils must determine what the problem is asking and, in many cases, carry out more than one type of calculation to find solutions. Analysis of the problems reveals that some contain additional information that is not needed.

Materials can be used to assist with the calculation if necessary, as the focus of the problems is about reading for information and determining what the question is asking rather than computation or basic facts.

Discussion

Page 33

On this page pupils are given information that some problems require addition and some subtraction, but that only the subtraction problems are to be solved. This requires pupils to carefully analyse each story and determine what the problem is asking and whether addition or subtraction is needed to find the solution. This activity shifts the focus from having to find the answer to analysis of the problem and the importance of determining what the problem is asking.

Page 34

These problems involve multiplication and the wording and the steps involved have been kept fairly simple. Pupils may find it helpful to draw a diagram to work out what is happening in the story and determine what needs to be multiplied to find a solution. Some questions also require addition.

Page 35

This worksheet involves information about a pond with lily pads and ducks, with a number of interrelated questions based on the information. The questions begin with a set number of ducks and lily pads. Using this information as a basis, the amounts are changed to meet new criteria (lily pads flower, grow or die, and ducks fly in and out of the pond).

Pupils are required to keep track of the new information and use it to answer the subsequent questions.

Possible difficulties

- Inability to identify the need to add, subtract or multiply
- Confusion over whether to carry out more than one step to arrive at a solution
- Using all the numbers listed in the problem rather than just the numbers needed

Extension

- Explore the possibilities as to whether the dry season would be before or after the summer.
- Discuss how problems can have more than one answer depending on different interpretations.
- Pupils could write their own problems and give them to other pupils to solve.

KANGAROO MOBS

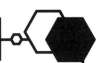

Look at the problems. Some use addition and some use subtraction. Solve only the subtraction problems.

1. There are 247 kangaroos at the waterhole. 119 kangaroos are drinking. How many kangaroos are not drinking?

_____

2. 135 kangaroos are eating grass and 164 kangaroos are sleeping under the trees. 59 more kangaroos start eating. How many kangaroos are eating?

_____

3. 264 kangaroos are sleeping under the shady trees. 128 kangaroos wake up. How many kangaroos are still sleeping?

_____

4. 172 adult kangaroos are by the river. 38 kangaroos have a joey in their pouch. How many kangaroos do not have a joey in their pouch?

_____

5. 162 kangaroos are eating grass and 148 kangaroos are sleeping under the trees. 59 more kangaroos go to sleep. How many kangaroos are sleeping?

_____

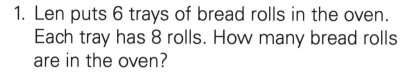

COOKING TIME

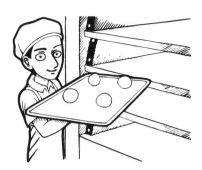

1. Len puts 6 trays of bread rolls in the oven. Each tray has 8 rolls. How many bread rolls are in the oven?

_____

2. Simone baked 8 trays of white bread loaves and 5 trays of brown bread loaves. Each tray had 10 loaves. How many loaves of white bread did she bake?

_____

3. Harry baked 5 trays of pies in the morning and 3 trays in the afternoon. Each tray had 6 pies. How many pies did he bake?

_____

4. Amira works 6 days each week at the bakery. She cooks 4 trays of biscuits each day. Each tray has 18 biscuits. How many biscuits does she cook each week?

_____

5. Jacky bakes 3 large trays of cakes and 4 small trays of cakes. The large trays have 20 cakes and the small trays have 12 cakes. How many cakes has he baked?

_____

Problem-solving in mathematics
www.prim-ed.com   Prim-Ed Publishing®

DUCK POND

A pond has 68 lily pads and 97 ducks.

1. During the day, each duck likes to rest on its own lily pad. How many ducks cannot rest on a lily pad?

   _____

2. 36 of the lily pads are in flower. If each lily pad has 3 flowers, how many flowers are there altogether?

   _____

3. How many lily pads are not in flower? _____

4. When the rains come, 23 more lily pads burst into flower. How many

   lily pads are now in flower? _____

5. During spring, 41 new lily pads grow and 28 lily pads die. How many

   lily pads are now on the lake? _____

6. Are there now enough lily pads for the ducks to rest on during the

   day?_____

7. During the dry summer, some ducks move to another pond. If 53 ducks moved to another pond, how many ducks stayed behind?

   _____

8. After the summer, 36 ducks fly away but 47 more ducks arrive. How many ducks are now at the pond?

   _____

Problem-solving

To solve problems involving distance and map reading.

Curriculum links

England (Year 3)

- Using and applying: Solve one-step and two-step problems involving numbers and measures, choosing and carrying out appropriate calculations.
- Calculating: Add and subtract mentally.
- Calculating: Use written methods to add and subtract.

Northern Ireland (Key Stage 1)

- Processes in maths: Select the mathematics appropriate for a task.
- Processes in maths: Develop different approaches to problem solving.
- Number: Understand the operations of addition and subtraction, and use them to solve problems.
- Number: Know addition and subtraction facts.
- Number: Develop strategies for adding and subtracting mentally.

Scotland (First)

- +/-/x/÷: Use addition and subtraction when solving problems, making best use of mental strategies and written skills developed.

Wales (Key Stage 2)

- Skills: Select and use the appropriate mathematics to solve problems in a variety of contexts.
- Skills: Identify and process the information needed to carry out work.
- Number: Use a variety of mental methods of computation and extend written methods.

Materials

Calculator, if needed

Focus

These pages explore finding and interpreting information from a map. Analysis of the map shows the distances between various birds' trees. Pupils are required to interpret this information and use it to find solutions. Some destinations are not direct and most have more than one possible route.

Discussion

Page 37

Pupils read and interpret questions and use information from the map to find solutions. Words such as 'shortest', 'longest', 'closest' and 'furthest' are used and, in some cases, pupils need to find all of the possible routes from one destination to another. The numbers have been kept simple to encourage mental computation and estimation.

Possible difficulties

- Inability to read the map and to use the information to find solutions
- Not knowing what to do when there is no direct route
- Confusion with the distance terms; e.g. furthest, closest

Extension

- Pupils can use the map and write questions for other pupils to solve.

BIRD TREES

When exploring the different ways to travel from tree to tree, each path can be walked along only once.

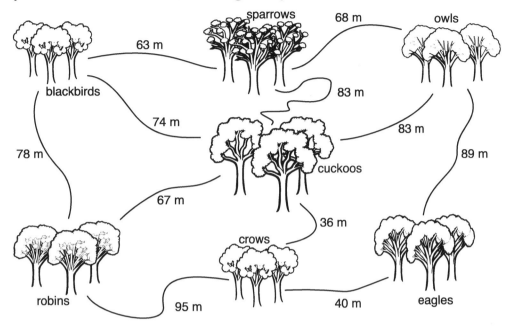

1. How far are the owls' trees from the crows' trees?

   _____

2. Which way is the shortest way from the robins' trees to the sparrows' trees?

   _____

3. How many ways can you go from the blackbirds' trees to the eagles' trees?

   _____

4. Which way is the shortest way from the blackbirds' trees to the crows' trees?

   _____

5. Which way is the longest way from the robins' trees to the owls' trees?

   _____

6. What birds' trees are closest to the cuckoos' trees?

   _____

7. What birds' trees are the furthest from the cuckoos' trees?

   _____

Problem-solving

To use spatial visualisation, logical reasoning and measurement to solve problems.

Curriculum links

England (Year 3)
- Using and applying: Solve one-step and two-step problems involving numbers and measures, choosing and carrying out appropriate calculations.
- Calculating: Add and subtract mentally.
- Calculating: Use written methods to add and subtract.
- Measuring: Read the time on an analogue clock.

Northern Ireland (Key Stage 1)
- Processes in maths: Select the mathematics appropriate for a task.
- Processes in maths: Develop different approaches to problem solving.
- Number: Understand the operations of addition and subtraction, and use them to solve problems.
- Number: Know addition and subtraction facts.
- Number: Develop strategies for adding and subtracting mentally.
- Measures: Recognise times on the analogue clock.

Scotland (First)
- +/-/x/÷: Use addition and subtraction when solving problems, making best use of mental strategies and written skills developed.
- Time: Tell the time using 12 and 24 hour clocks.

Wales (Key Stage 2)
- Skills: Select and use the appropriate mathematics to solve problems in a variety of contexts.
- Skills: Identify and process the information needed to carry out work.
- Number: Use a variety of mental methods of computation and extend written methods.
- Measures: Read times on digital clocks.

Materials

Calculator, digital clock

Focus

These pages explore different ways of visualising a problem and the various possibilities that may provide a solution. Logical reasoning, as well as an understanding of measurement (metres and centimetres), and digital time (using both 12-hour and 24-hour), is needed. With each problem, diagrams can be used to organise, sort and explore the data.

Discussion

Page 39
With these problems, pupils must visualise the paths that the animals take as they travel around the outside of each shape. An ability to convert from centimetres to metres and vice versa is also required.

In the first problem, the snail crawls around the garden more than once. It passes around corners A, B and C twice before coming to rest at D after having travelled 315 cm or 3 m 15 cm.

For the second problem, the addition required to keep track of the centipede's progress is more complex. However, some pupils may realise that the length of the short and long sides combined is 125 cm and use this to calculate that the distance to reach D a second time is 375 cm. When the centipede travels a further 85 cm, it will have travelled 460 cm or 4 m 60 cm and stop at C.

The last problem is more difficult as not all of the lengths are given and must be calculated first from the information provided on the diagram.

Page 40
To solve these problems, pupils explore the relationships among the numbers on each pan of the balance and then compare the weight of one pan to the other. Estimation could be used, or the sum on each side can be used to solve which number needs to be subtracted to make the pans balance.

Page 41
This page explores pupils' understanding of digital time as they investigate the ways the digits can be placed to show different times and read the times to compare which is earliest and latest. The way in which zero is used on a digital clock also needs to be considered. In Problem 2, there are only four possibilities (as there cannot be 90 or 95 minutes), but 0 can be used to show the hour after midnight (if using 24-hour time). In Problem 3, there are more possibilities when 24-hour time is considered and zero can be used in all possible positions. The final question requires interpretation of the possible times. Discuss 24-hour time e.g. Why does a new day begin in the middle of the night?

Possible difficulties

- Unable to convert centimetres to metres and centimetres
- Confusion about moving along a side more than once
- Not calculating the sides whose length is not given
- Not understanding 24-hour time

Extension

- Pupils could write their own problems involving distance around a shape (perimeter), numbers on a balance, or time, and give them to other pupils to solve.
- Investigate further facts about the calendar—why is the tenth month named October?; which two consecutive months have the same number of days and why? Is 1 July the halfway point of a calendar year?

D ───── 45 cm ───── C

A
Start ⟶
B

1. A snail crawls 3 m 15 cm around a square garden.

   At which corner will it stop?

   _____

2. A centipede shuffles 4 m 60 cm around a rectangular garden.

   At which corner will it stop?

   _____

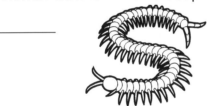

D ───── 85 cm ───── C

40 cm

A
⟵ Start
B

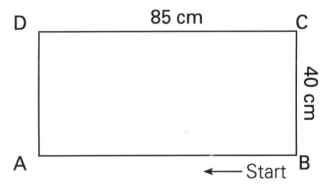

F   E

55 cm

D   65 cm   C

30 cm

A   90 cm   B

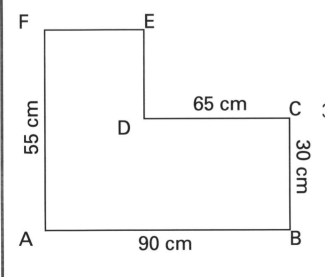

3. An ant walked clockwise around this garden. Starting at A, it stopped the third time it reached D.

   How far did it walk?

   _____

BALANCE THE BOOKS

Which book would you take off the scale to make it balance?

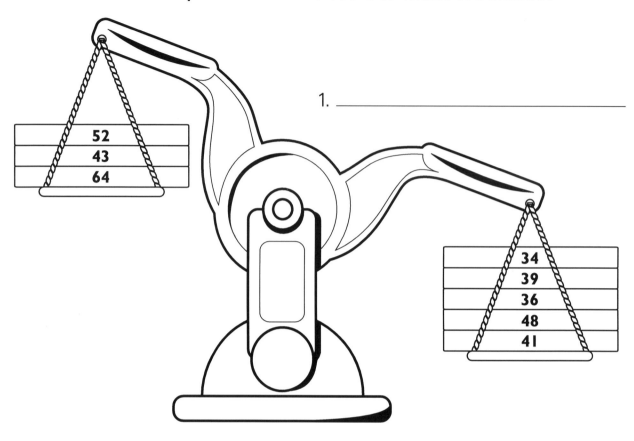

1. _____

| 52 |
| 43 |
| 64 |

| 34 |
| 39 |
| 36 |
| 48 |
| 41 |

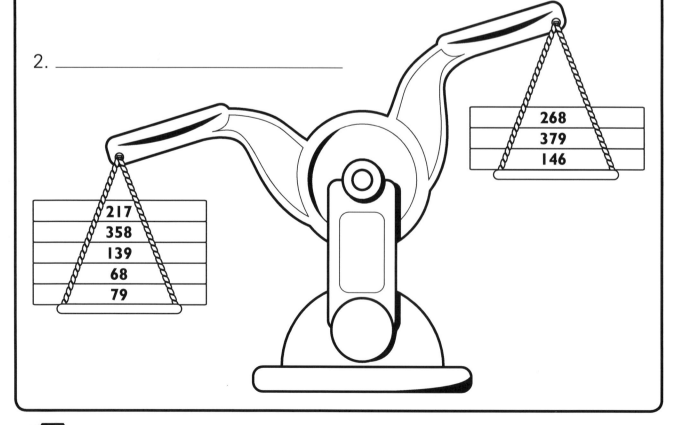

2. _____

| 268 |
| 379 |
| 146 |

| 217 |
| 358 |
| 139 |
| 68 |
| 79 |

1. (a) A digital clock shows hours and minutes. What times can be shown using only the digits 3, 4 and 5?

  (b) What is the latest time? _____

  (c) What is the earliest time? _____

2. (a) What times can be shown using only the digits 0, 5, 9?

  (b) What is the latest time? _____

  (c) What is the earliest time? _____

3. (a) What would be the times if you used 0, 1, 2 and 3?

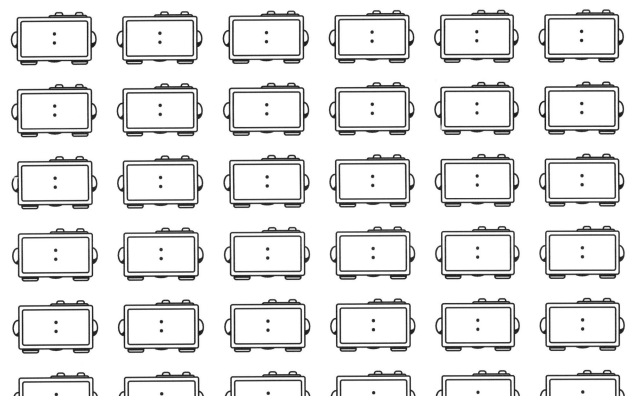

  (b) What are the earliest and latest times? _____ _____

Problem-solving

To organise data and make predictions.

Curriculum links

England (Year 3)

- Using and applying: Solve one-step and two-step problems involving numbers and measures, choosing and carrying out appropriate calculations.
- Using and applying: Represent the information in a problem using diagrams, use these to find a solution and present it in context.
- Calculating: Add and subtract mentally.
- Calculating: Use written methods to add and subtract.

Northern Ireland (Key Stage 1)

- Processes in maths: Select the mathematics appropriate for a task.
- Processes in maths: Develop different approaches to problem solving.
- Processes in maths: Organise work and work systematically.
- Number: Understand the operations of addition and subtraction, and use them to solve problems.
- Number: Know addition and subtraction facts.
- Number: Develop strategies for adding and subtracting mentally.

Scotland (First)

- +/-/x/÷: Use addition and subtraction when solving problems, making best use of mental strategies and written skills developed.

Wales (Key Stage 2)

- Skills: Select and use the appropriate mathematics to solve problems in a variety of contexts.
- Skills: Identify and process the information needed to carry out work.
- Number: Use a variety of mental methods of computation and extend written methods.

Materials

Counters or a calculator, if needed

Focus

These pages explore different ways data can be analysed and recorded. In each situation, diagrams, tables and lists can be used to organise and sort the data in order to make predictions for further analysis and exploration. Visualisation and logical reasoning are involved in these investigations.

Discussion

Page 43

A list has been provided to help pupils manage the different possibilities. The questions about there being two, three and four fillings are designed to make pupils think about whether there will be more, fewer or the same number of sandwiches, and to explore the pattern of what

happens as the number of fillings increase. As the number of fillings increase, the number of sandwich rolls or wraps that can be made decreases.

Page 44

Analysis of these problems reveals that the distance travelled involves movement both forwards and backwards. The first problem involves a snail climbing forwards a distance of 7 metres and then slipping back 2 metres, so the distance travelled each day is 5 metres. Since the pipe is 15 metres high, it will take exactly three days to reach the top.

The next question is similar, but in this case the time will not be exact. Since the well is 39 metres deep and the travel distance is 6 metres every two hours, it will take 14 hours to reach the top (with not all of the last two hours needed, since only 3 metres needs to be travelled, not 6 metres). The last question entails a distance travelled of 2 metres every hour and 10 minutes on the way up and 3 metres every hour and 30 minutes on the way down.

Page 45

Using a table and listing possibilities while using the 'try and adjust' strategy is a popular way of finding solutions to these types of problems. This involves trying a combination and putting it in a table and then adjusting accordingly. The first example has two possible combinations, as it involves multiples of six and 10. This results in 10 bags of six and three bags of ten or five bags of six and six bags of 10 to make a total of 90 oranges.

Question 2 involves multiples of two and four, since there are many different combinations that work; for example, two puppies and 10 budgies, three puppies and eight budgies. At first glance the last question has two possible answers. It involves multiples of five and 12, which leads to two boxes of twelve and 15 boxes of five or seven boxes of twelve and three boxes of five. However, when the information of 'more than 10 boxes' is taken into consideration then there is only one possibility, since the second example uses only 10 boxes.

Possible difficulties

- Not using a table or list to manage the data
- Not seeing that, for example, a ham and cheese sandwich is the same as a cheese and ham sandwich
- Confusion working out how far was really travelled when moving both forwards and backwards
- Not considering that more than 10 boxes were used

Extension

- Make a table showing the combinations of one filling, two fillings, three fillings, and so on.
- Make a table showing how far was travelled each day/hour.
- Draw and label a diagram to show the combinations of how many oranges, and so forth.

PARTY FOOD

Maddy and Mandy are making food for a party. They are making sandwiches, rolls and wraps.

We have bread, rolls and wraps.

We have ham, cheese, tomato and lettuce.

1. Write all of the different sandwiches, rolls and wraps they can make if they only use two fillings.

Sandwiches	Rolls	Wraps
_____	_____	_____
_____	_____	_____
_____	_____	_____
_____	_____	_____
_____	_____	_____
_____	_____	_____

2. Write all of the different ways they can use three fillings.

Sandwiches	Rolls	Wraps
_____	_____	_____
_____	_____	_____
_____	_____	_____
_____	_____	_____

What happens if they use three fillings? _____

What would happen if they used all of the fillings? _____

1. A drainpipe is 15 metres long. Each day, a snail climbs 7 metres up the spout but then slips back 2 metres overnight. How long will it take for the snail to reach the top of the drainpipe?

_____

_____

2. A green frog is at the bottom of a well. Every two hours he climbs up 8 metres but also slips back 2 metres. If the well is 39 metres deep, how long will it take for the frog to get out of the well?

_____

_____

3. A caterpillar climbs up a tree, eating leaves on the way. Each hour, it crawls 2 metres up the tree and then eats leaves for 10 minutes. If the tree is 19 metres high, how long will it take for the caterpillar to reach the top?

_____

_____

4. When climbing down from the top of the tree, the caterpillar slides down 3 metres each hour and then rests for 30 minutes. How long will it take for the caterpillar to reach the ground?

_____

_____

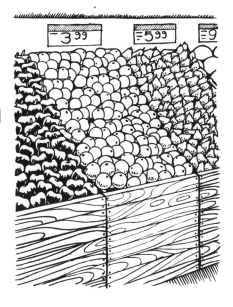

1. A fruit shop has 90 oranges available to sell. Some are packed in bags of six and others in bags of ten. How many are there of each size of bag?

_____

_____

2. The pet shop has budgies and puppies on display in the window. Combined, the owner counted a total of 28 legs on the pets. How many puppies and how many budgies could there be?

_____

_____

3. The chocolate shop packages chocolates in both a small box that holds 5 chocolates and a larger box that holds 12 chocolates. The shop assistant packed 99 chocolates and used more than 10 boxes. How many of each size box did he use?

_____

_____

Problem-solving
To use spatial visualisation and logical reasoning to solve problems.

Curriculum links
England (Year 3)
- Using and applying: Identify patterns and relationships involving shapes and use these to solve problems.
- Understanding shape: Draw and make 2-D shapes and 3-D solids.

Northern Ireland (Key Stage 1)
- Processes in maths: Develop different approaches to problem solving.
- Processes in maths: Recognise simple patterns and relationships.
- Shape and space: Make constructions and patterns using 2-D and 3-D shapes.

Scotland (First)
- Patterns and relationships: Continue and devise repeating patterns.
- Properties of 2-D shapes and 3-D objects: Explore simple 3-D objects and 2-D shapes.

Wales (Key Stage 2)
- Skills: Select and use the appropriate mathematics to solve problems in a variety of contexts.
- Skills: Recognise patterns that arise in spatial situations.
- Skills: Visualise shapes.
- Shape, position and movement: Make 2-D and 3-D shapes and patterns with increasing accuracy.

Materials
Toothpicks; cubes, such as wooden or multilink cubes or Unifix™, in two different colours; isometric grid paper

Focus
These pages explore possible arrangements of two-dimensional and three-dimensional shapes to determine how particular outcomes are formed. Spatial as well as logical thinking and organisation are involved as pupils investigate all likely arrangements to ensure the final shapes match the given criteria or visualise a given shape in terms of its component parts.

Discussion
Page 47
Pupils will need to manipulate the toothpicks to see how each shape can be extended using as small a number of toothpicks as possible. The original triangle is used as a building block for the larger shapes and triangles that are formed, but the number of toothpicks used for the new shapes is not simply a multiple of the three used for the first shape.

Increasing the size of the square can be considered in a similar way, using four, then 12, then 24 toothpicks, and so on. The problem could also simply imply that the number of toothpicks on the sides of the square increase, using 4, 8, 12 and so on.

Both solutions are reasonable, based on an analysis of the problem, and should be discussed with the class.

Page 48
Pupils will need to manipulate blocks to see if they can create shapes that look like those depicted on the page, building an ability to visualise three-dimensional shapes. Some may need to draw lines on the shapes in order to see how the blocks can be used to form the shapes. Building a larger cube extends the thinking introduced on page 47.

Making it in two colours introduces another aspect of visualisation, especially when a larger cube is constructed. The number of cubes needed increases in ways that at first might seem surprising.

Page 49
The drawings of the shapes on this page reverse the type of thinking needed when building shapes so that patterns can be seen. In these examples, the cubes that are partly hidden must be visualised and careful analysis is needed to consider the whole divided into its component parts in order to determine the number of cubes used.

Possible difficulties
- Focusing only on building exact replicas of the triangle or square and using more toothpicks than needed
- Unable to visualise the three-dimensional cubes in their representations on the two-dimensional page
- Considering only those cubes that can be readily seen

Extension
- Have pupils make other shapes using five cubes, and have other pupils copy them.
- Make stacks of cubes for other pupils to replicate. The number of cubes used should be specified.
- Have pupils use isometric paper to draw the shapes they make, and have other pupils copy them.

TOOTHPICKS

1. Use three toothpicks to make a triangle.

   Now make 2 triangles using 5 toothpicks.

   Make 3 triangles.

   How many toothpicks did you need? _____

   Draw it.

   Use two more toothpicks to make a larger triangle.

   Now make an even larger triangle.

   How many toothpicks did you need? _____

   Draw it.

2. Use four toothpicks to make a square.

   How many toothpicks do you need to make a larger square? _____

   Make an even larger square.

   How many toothpicks did you need? _____

   Draw it.

BUILDING WITH CUBES

Find some cubes in two different colours.

Can you make these shapes using five cubes?

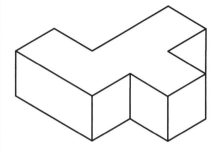
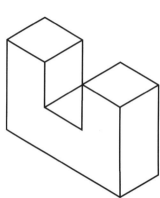
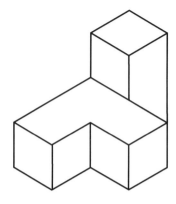

Use your cubes to build a larger cube.

1. How many cubes did you need?

   _____

2. Can you make a cube that is half one colour and half another colour?

   _____

   _____

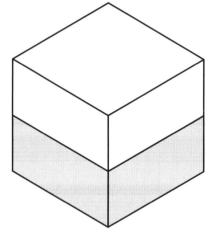

3. How many cubes of each colour did you need?

   _____

4. Can you make a similar cube that is a larger size?

   _____

   _____

5. How many cubes of each colour did you need? _____

STACKING CUBES

1. This set of stairs is made by stacking cubes. How many cubes are needed to make the stairs?

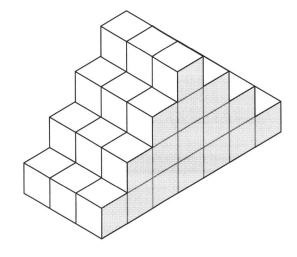

   _____

   Find as many cubes as you think you need and make the staircase.

2. How many cubes are needed to make this shape?

   _____

   Take as many cubes as you think you need and make the shape.

3. How many cubes are in this pyramid?

   _____

4. How many cubes would you need in total to put one cube on top and one more layer on the bottom?

   _____

   Make the new shape to see if you were correct.

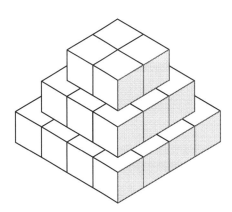

Problem-solving

To use strategic thinking to solve problems.

Curriculum links

England (Year 3)
- Using and applying: Solve one-step and two-step problems involving money, choosing and carrying out appropriate calculations.
- Calculating: Add and subtract mentally.
- Calculating: Use written methods to explain addition, subtraction and multiplication.

Northern Ireland (Key Stage 1)
- Processes in maths: Select the mathematics appropriate for a task.
- Processes in maths: Develop different approaches to problem solving.
- Number: Understand the operations of addition, subtraction and multiplication, and use them to solve problems.
- Number: Know addition, subtraction and multiplication facts.
- Number: Develop strategies for adding and subtracting mentally.
- Number: Add and subtract money and solve money problems.

Scotland (First)
- =/–/x/÷: Use addition, subtraction and multiplication when solving problems, making best use of mental strategies developed.
- Money: Use money.

Wales (Key Stage 2)
- Skills: Select and use the appropriate mathematics to solve problems in a variety of contexts.
- Skills: Identify and process the information needed to carry out work.
- Number: Use a variety of mental methods of computation.
- Measures and money: Solve problems involving money.

Materials

Counters

Focus

This page explores problems in which it seems there could be several answers but analysis of the connections among the data reveals there is a unique solution. A process of 'try and adjust' could be used; however, logical reasoning of the possibilities and then using a table, diagram or materials to organise them will be more productive. This will lead to the development of ways of thinking that can be generalised to other complex problems.

Discussion

Page 51

Several methods can be used to try and solve these problems. For Problem 1, since there are 99 people altogether, not all tables can seat five since 99 is not a multiple of five. All of the tables can seat three, but this will only give seating for 75 people. The remaining 24 people must be seated at tables of five. Putting 2 more at each of the tables gives 12 tables with five people and 13 tables with three people (a total of 99).

Another way would be to put multiples of three or five into a table or diagram (similar to page 43) and systematically check the remaining numbers until a solution is reached. The 9 in the ones place of 99 can be made with the addition of 4 and 5, which suggests 8 tables of three and 15 tables of five; or 18 tables of three and 9 tables of five; or 23 tables of three and 2 tables of five. However, all three answers violate one of the criteria set.

Nine can also be made with 0 and 9, leading to 13 tables of three and 12 tables of five, or 3 tables of three and 18 tables of five. However, only 13 tables of three and 12 tables of five uses 25 tables and gives a total of 99 people. Counters can also be used to model the problem, again focusing on groups of three and groups of five.

The second problem can be considered in a similar manner—adjusting an answer given by first considering all tickets at one price or analysing the total amount of money raised by using multiples of 2 and 5 and using a table, diagram or counters.

Possible difficulties

- Not using a table or diagram to manage the data
- Not considering that exactly 25 tables are needed in the first question or that £95 is needed in the second question

Extension

- Discuss the various methods used by pupils to solve the problems. Include the ones discussed above.
- Construct other problems using the same form of complex reasoning for pupils to solve.

HOW MANY?

1. A cafe has 25 tables. Some tables seat 3 people and others seat 5 people. The waiter saw that all the seats were taken. If there were 99 people at the cafe, how many tables for three were there?

2. Tickets for the school concert cost £2 for children and £5 for adults. Pupils in Year 3 sold 31 tickets and raised £95. How many of each type of ticket did they sell?

SOLUTIONS

Note: Many solutions are written statements rather than simply numbers. This is to encourage teachers and students to solve problems in this way.

LARGER SHAPES .... page 3

Shape 1

Shape 2

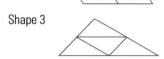

Shape 3

GRID FUN 1 .... page 4

Teacher check

GRID FUN 2 .... page 5

Teacher check

THE BIG RACE .... page 7

1. 8th position
2. 9 cars

WHAT'S MY NUMBER? .... page 9

1. 739
2. 536
3. Teacher check

MISSING NUMBERS .... page 10

1. (a) 8
   (b) 4
   (c) 5
   (d) 43
   (e) 10

2.

	Joseph	Jacob	Jonathan
Age	10	5	8
Year level	6	1	4

3. Teacher check

WHAT'S MY AGE? .... page 11

1. 7
2. 16
3. 5
4. 6
5. 6
6. 12
7. 15

AT THE BEACH .... page 13

1. 34 people
2. 27 people

3. 51 surfers
4. 19 people
5. 11 surfers

AT THE PARTY .... page 14

1. 82 sausage rolls
2. 70 party pies
3. 25 more meatballs
4. (a) 52 soft drinks
   (b) 82 drinks

IN THE GARDEN .... page 15

1. 261 tomatoes
2. 150 lettuces
3. 112 tomatoes
4. 180 lettuces
5. 96 lettuces
6. 92 tomatoes

HOW MANY DIGITS? .... page 17

1. (a) 118   (b) 140
2. (a) less   (b) 19   (c) 41
3. 3 and 5 – say 18 times, write 40 times
   4, 6, 7, 8 and 9 – say 40 times, write 40 times

TANGRAMS 1 .... page 19

1.

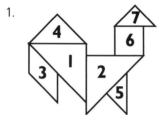

2.

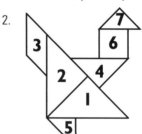

TANGRAMS 2 .... page 20

1.

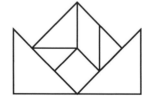

Note: Many solutions are written statements rather than simply numbers. This is to encourage teachers and students to solve problems in this way.

2.

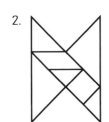

TANGRAMS 3 .... page 21

1.

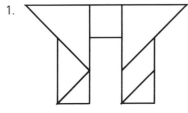

2.

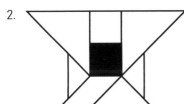

MAGIC SQUARES 1 .... page 23

1. 12

2. (a)

8	1	6
3	5	7
4	9	2

15

(b)

11	4	9
6	8	10
7	12	5

24

(c)

32	4	24
12	20	28
16	36	8

60

(d)

4	9	8
11	7	3
6	5	10

21

MAGIC SQUARES 2 .... page 24

1. (a)

4	3	8
9	5	1
2	7	6

15

(b)

15	1	11
5	9	13
7	17	3

27

(c)

10	3	8
5	7	9
6	11	4

21

2. (a)

5	4	9
10	6	2
3	8	7

18

(b)

16	2	12
6	10	14
8	18	4

30

(c)

11	4	9
6	8	10
7	12	5

24

(d) Yes

3. (a)

7	6	11
12	8	4
5	10	9

24

(b)

18	4	14
8	12	16
10	20	6

36

(c)

13	6	11
8	10	12
9	14	7

30

(d) Yes

MAGIC CIRCLES .... page 25

1.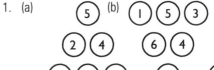

(a) 5 / 2 4 / 3 6 1

(b) 1 5 3 / 6 4 / 2

(c) 4 / 2 3 / 6 1 5

2.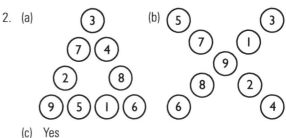

(a) 3 / 7 4 / 2 8 / 9 5 1 6

(b) 5 3 / 7 1 / 9 / 8 2 / 6 4

(c) Yes

TUCKSHOP .... page 27

1. Yes. They cost £5
2. No. They cost £10
3. £4
4. £4
5. Answers will vary – e.g. 3 egg sandwiches and 3 apple juices
6. Answers will vary – e.g. 1 chicken roll, 1 choc milk

WINDOW PANES 1 .... page 29

1.

R G	R G	R Y	R Y	R B
B Y	Y B	B G	G B	Y G

R B	B G	B G	B Y	B Y
G Y	R Y	Y R	R G	G R

B R	B R	G R	G B	G B
G R	Y G	Y B	Y R	R Y

G Y	G Y	Y R	Y B	Y G
R B	B R	G B	R G	B R

Y R	Y B	Y G	G R	
B G	G R	R B	B Y	

2. 24

SOLUTIONS

Note: Many solutions are written statements rather than simply numbers. This is to encourage teachers and students to solve problems in this way.

DRIVE TIME .... page 30

1. 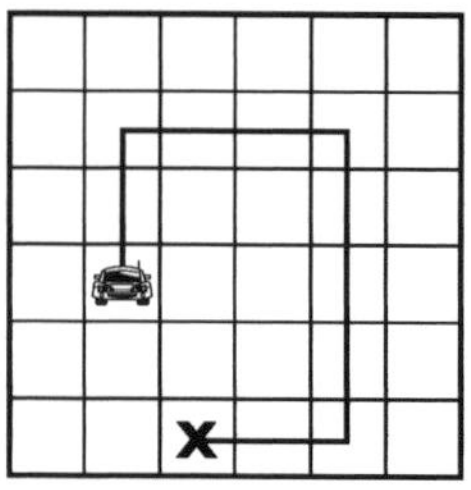
2. 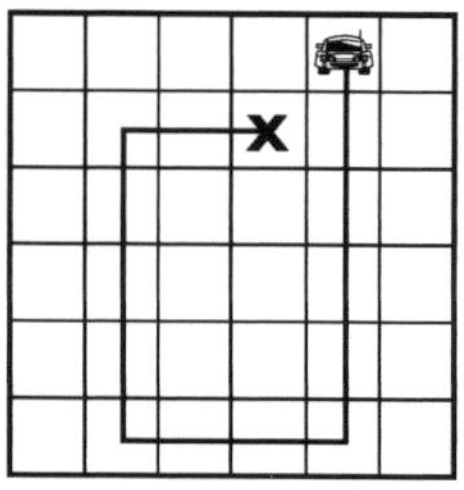
3. 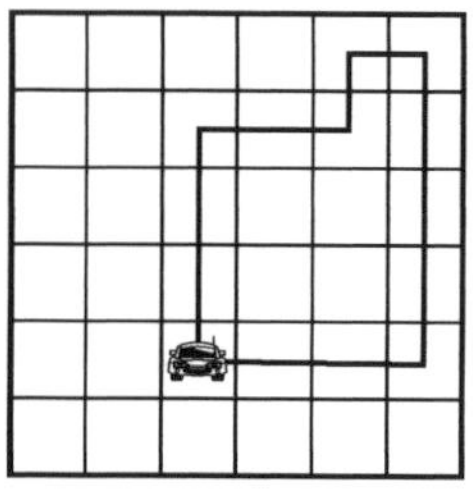
4.

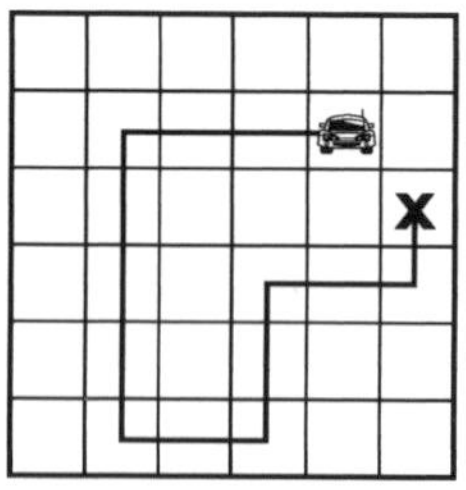

WINDOW PANES 2 .... page 31

1.

R R		R R		B B		B B
R B		B R		B R		R B
B B		B B		R R		R R

R B		B R		R B		B R
R B		B R		B R		R B
R B		B R		R B		B R

R R		R R		B B		B B
B B		B B		R R		R R
B R		R B		R B		B R

R B		B R		B R		R B
R R		R R		B B		B B
B B		B B		R R		R R

R B		B R		B R		R B
R B		B R		R B		B R
B R		R B		R B		B R

2. 20

KANGAROO MOBS .... page 33

1. 128 kangaroos
2. addition (no need to answer)
3. 136 kangaroos
4. 134 kangaroos
5. addition (no need to answer)

COOKING TIME .... page 34

1. 48 bread rolls
2. 80 loaves
3. 48 pies
4. 432 biscuits
5. 108 cakes

DUCK POND .... page 35

1. 29 ducks
2. 108 flowers
3. 32 lily pads
4. 59 lily pads
5. 81 lily pads
6. No. There are 16 pads too few.
7. 44 ducks
8. 55 ducks

BIRD TREES .... page 37

1. 119 m (shortest route)
2. robins ➡ blackbirds ➡ sparrows (141 m)
3. At least 10 different ways
4. blackbirds ➡ cuckoos ➡ crows (110 m)
5. robins ➡ blackbirds ➡ sparrows ➡ cuckoos ➡ crows ➡ eagles ➡ owls (389 m)
6. crows
7. sparrows and owls

ANIMAL TRAILS .... page 39

1. D
2. D
3. 7 m 65 cm (765 cm)

BALANCE THE BOOKS .... page 40

1. 39
2. 68

TAKING TIME .... page 41

1. (a) 3:45 3:54 4:35 4:53 5:34 5:43
   (b) 5.43 (12-hr)
   (c) 3.45 (12-hr)
2. (a) 0:59 5:09 9:05 9:50 ☐ ☐
   (b) 9.50 (12-hr)
   (c) 0.59 (24-hr)
3. (a)
   0:12 0:13 0:21 0:23 0:31 0:32
   1:02 1:03 1:20 1:30 1:23 1:32
   2:01 2:03 2:10 2:30 2:13 2:31
   3:01 3:03 3:10 3:20 3:12 3:21
   10:23 10:32 12:03 12:30 13:02 13:20
   21:03 21:30 23:01 23:10 23:13 20:31

Note: Many solutions are written statements rather than simply numbers. This is to encourage teachers and students to solve problems in this way.

(b) 0:12 and 23:13.

PARTY FOOD .... page 43

1. (a) ham/cheese
      ham/tomato
      ham/lettuce
      cheese/tomato
      cheese/lettuce
      tomato/lettuce

   (b) ham/cheese
       ham/tomato
       ham/lettuce
       cheese/tomato
       cheese/lettuce
       tomato/lettuce

   (c) ham/cheese
       ham/tomato
       ham/lettuce
       cheese/tomato
       cheese/lettuce
       tomato/lettuce

2. (a) ham/cheese/tomato
       ham/cheese/lettuce
       ham/tomato/lettuce
       cheese/tomato/lettuce

   (b) ham/cheese/tomato
       ham/cheese/lettuce
       ham/tomato/lettuce
       cheese/tomato/lettuce

   (c) ham/cheese/tomato
       ham/cheese/lettuce
       ham/tomato/lettuce
       cheese/tomato/lettuce

   (d) Can only make 12 different snacks
   (e) Can only make 3 different snacks

HOW LONG? .... page 44

1. 3 days
2. 14 hours – not all of the last 2 hours is needed
3. 12 hours – not all of the last hour is needed
4. 10 hours 30 minutes – not all of the time is needed

AT THE SHOPS .... page 45

1. 10 bags of six and three bags of 10; or
   five bags of six and six bags of 10
2. Answers will vary. Combinations include:

Puppies–4 legs	2	3	4	5	6
Budgies–2 legs	10	8	6	4	2

3. two boxes of 12, 15 boxes of five

TOOTHPICKS .... page 47

1. (a)   (b)

(c) 7

(d) 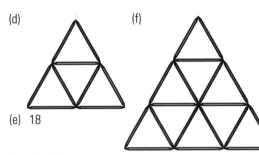 (f)

(e) 18

2. (a) 8 or 12

   (b)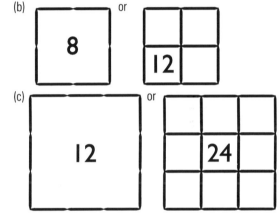

   (c)

BUILDING WITH CUBES .... page 48

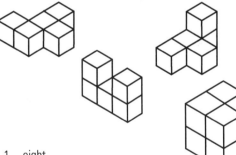

1. eight
2. Yes, with a total of eight cubes
3. Four of each colour
4. Yes, with a total of 64 cubes
5. 32

STACKING CUBES .... page 49

1. 48
2. 27
3. 29
4. 55

HOW MANY? .... page 51

1. 12 tables of five people and 13 tables of three people
2. 11 adults and 20 children

TANGRAM RESOURCE PAGE

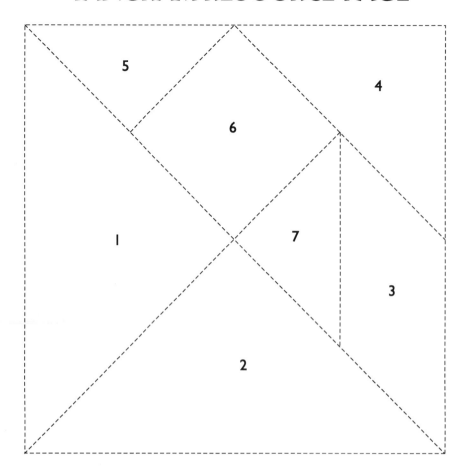

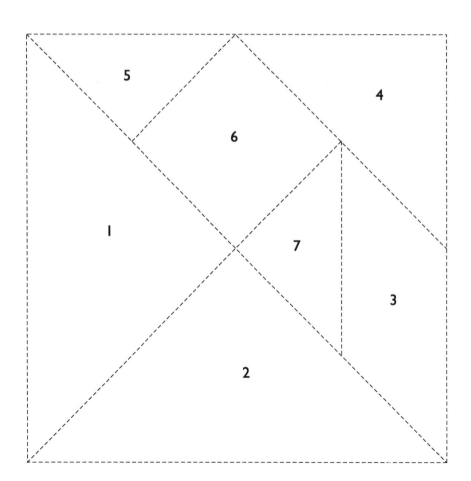

10 mm x 10 mm GRID RESOURCE PAGE

15 mm x 15 mm GRID RESOURCE PAGE

Problem-solving in mathematics

www.prim-ed.com   Prim-Ed Publishing®

TRIANGULAR GRID RESOURCE PAGE

TRIANGULAR ISOMETRIC RESOURCE PAGE

SQUARE ISOMETRIC RESOURCE PAGE

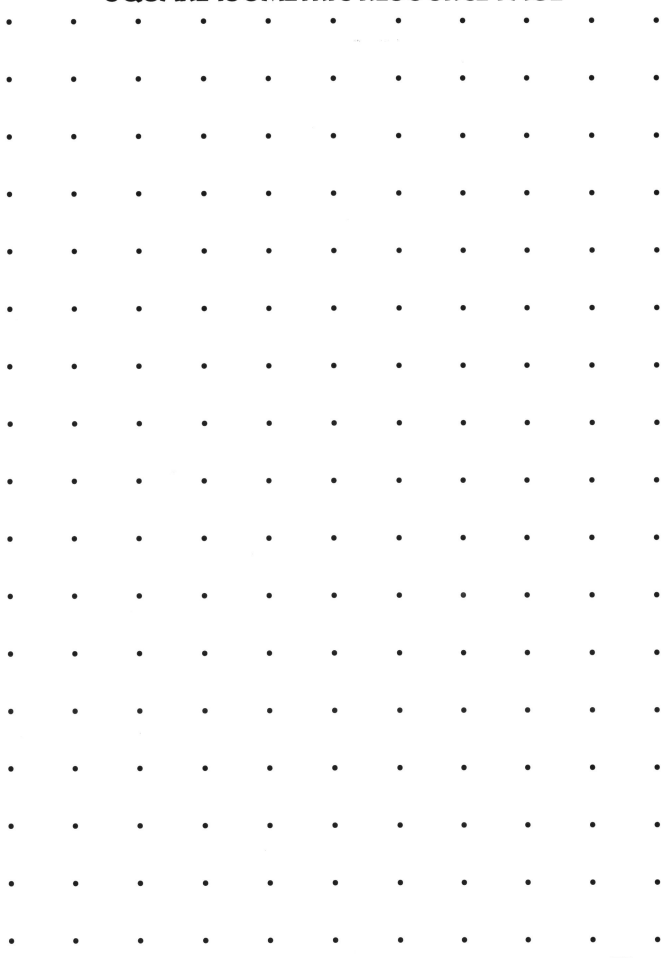

4-DIGIT NUMBER EXPANDER RESOURCE PAGE (x 5)

ones

tens

hundreds

thousands

ones

tens

hundreds

thousands